FOR PARTIES,
GATHERINGS OF TWO OR THREE FRIENDS,
YOUR OWN, PERSONAL PLEASURE—

there is no other folk song book
like this one. It is a strong,
balanced and vital cross section
of the best in folk music, from
all times and places—additionally
it teaches you to play the guitar.

A little study and practice with
the section in the back of this
book, called "The Beginner Folk-Guitarist,"
and soon you will be able to accompany
any song in the collection.

Enjoy and use this unique book!
No one who loves folk songs should be
without

A NEW TREASURY OF FOLK SONGS

"Here's to ya
And toahds ya
If I hadn't-a seed ya
I wouldn't-a knowed ya."

COMPILED AND ARRANGED BY
TOM GLAZER

A NEW TREASURY OF FOLK SONGS

WITH: AN INTRODUCTION TO FOLK-GUITAR
ACCOMPANIMENT FOR THE BEGINNER

A NEW TREASURY OF FOLK SONGS

Bantam Reference Library edition published May 1961
2nd printing..................October 1962
3rd printing................September 1963
New Bantam edition published November 1964

Library of Congress Catalog Card Number M61-1002

Contents

Introduction	vii	Go Tell Aunt Rhody	57
Acres of Clams	2	Goin' Down the Road	58
Barbara Allen	4	Got An Old Mule	60
The Bennington Rifles	6	The Gray Goose	62
Black Is the Color	8	Greensleeves	64
Blow the Candles Out	9	Hallelujah, I'm a Bum	66
Blow the Man Down	11	The Hammer Song	68
Blow Ye Winds of the Morning	13	Haul Away, Joe	70
The Blue-tail Fly	15	Henry Martin	72
Careless Love	18	He's Got the Whole World	74
Cindy	19	Home on the Range	76
Colorado Trail	21	I Know My Love	78
Cotton-eyed Joe	22	I Know Where I'm Goin'	80
Crawdad	23	I Ride an Old Paint	82
The Dodger	25	I'm Gone Away	84
Down in the Valley	28	Jennie Jenkins	86
Drill Ye Tarriers	30	Jessie James	88
The Drunken Sailor	32	John Henry	90
The E-ri-e	34	Johnny Has Gone For a Soldier	92
Every Night When the Sun Goes Down	36	Joshua Fought the Battle of Jericho	93
Fare Thee Well, O Honey	38	The Keeper	95
The Farmer	39	The Leather-Winged Bat	98
The Farmer's Cursed Wife	41	Little Bitty Baby	100
The Fireship	43	Lord Randal	102
The Foggy Dew	46	The Midnight Special	104
Frankie and Johnnie	48	Motherless Child	106
The Frog Went A-Courtin'	51	Oh Freedom	108
Git Along Little Dogies	53	Old Smoky	110
Go Down, Moses	55	Paper of Pins	112

Pat Works on the Railway	114	Tam Pierce	138
Peter Grey	116	The Trail to Mexico	140
The Riddle Song	118	The Twelve Days of Christmas	142
The Roving Gambler	120	Uncle Reuben	145
Shenando'	122	Venezuela	147
Skip to My Lou	124	Wayfaring Stranger	149
Sourwood Mountain	126	A Worried Man	151
The Sow Got the Measles	128	Yankee Doodle	153
Spanish Is the Loving Tongue	130	So We'll Go No More A-Roving	156
Springfield Mountain	132	Tibbie Dunbar	158
The Streets of Laredo	134	With Rue My Heart Is Laden	160
Sweet Betsy from Pike	136	The Beginner Folk-Guitarist	162

Introduction

What is a folk song? Are Stephen Foster's songs folk songs? George Gershwin's *Porgy and Bess* is called a "folk opera"; are the songs in *Porgy and Bess* folk songs? Can a "pop" song become a folk song? Are hillbilly songs folk songs?

If we can answer the first question we can answer the rest. There are many definitions of a folk song; here is mine. I believe it is accurate and scientific in the sense that it attempts to describe an objective situation rather than subjective likes and dislikes. It is this: a folk song is almost any song which is liked by almost everybody in the country of its origin over a long period of time. This rules out: (1) songs which are or were popular for just a short time, (2) songs which may become folk songs but are not yet old enough and (3) songs which are liked by a minority of the population rather than a majority.

Examples of number one fill the old songbooks. Examples of number two are tunes like some of the older "pop" songs such as "Alexander's Ragtime Band," "Down By the Old Mill Stream," and others, which seem to be becoming folk songs. Examples of number three are art songs, most operatic arias, and the more esoteric "pop" songs.

Accordingly, then, we can answer the other often-asked questions above. Stephen Foster's songs (the famous ones) are folk songs. The songs in *Porgy and Bess* are not *yet* folk songs; they may, if they remain popular enough for a long enough time, become folk songs. (The term "folk opera" for *Porgy and Bess* is a loose one; it refers to the *sources* of the music and story.) A "pop" song can become a folk song. Some hillbilly songs are folk songs, others are not. I feel that the term "hillbilly" describes more a style of playing than a type of song, though there are or used to be exceptions. Today the hillbilly song is giving way to the "Rockabilly" or "Rock and Roll" song, which I feel reflect musically the gradual integration of the Negro and white races.

Another frequently asked question is, "Where does that song come from?" In most cases folk songs are traced to one or more collectors who simply collected them from one or more individuals, who, in turn, learned them from someone else and so on back to someone dead and gone.

We in the field are often confronted with the word "authentic," used for a song or a singer or a way of playing an instrument. The question is a ticklish one. I don't think that "authenticity" is an objective state of grace or a heaven which only true folk believers achieve; it is a relative term and quite subject to the whims of taste. I have noted the following implied or stated definitions of authenticity in the folk field: (1) regional mannerisms, vocal and instrumental, (2) the first version a person ever heard of a song, (3) the Southern accent, and (4) authenticity is in inverse proportion to literacy.

Is there no authenticity then? I think the word is bad. There are *styles* of singing and playing, and these styles can be handed down traditionally, but they can and do change. You may like your song sung one way or twenty ways; which is authentic for you? While the undoubted charms of regionalisms exist, a naive, ungrammatical, untrained, unself-conscious method of singing is not the only way; nor, on the other hand, should folk songs be restricted to the concert hall or the picket line.

The songs in this book are, I believe, a strong cross section of the best-liked songs in America today. Most are well-known; a few may not be. Three are not folk songs at all; I explain them further on. I must underline the seeming paradox that to put a folk song on paper is almost to kill it dead, because a written song can only approximate the way or ways it can be sung or played or heard. Your favorite version may not be here; mine are—I had no other choice.

The songs are arranged alphabetically, unlike most collections where songs are at times rather unnaturally placed into odd categories. While there *are* cowboy songs and sailor songs and work songs, and spirituals, what precisely are "social" songs, "hallelujahs," "whoppers," "make-believe," etc.?

At the back of the book is a regrettably short introduction to beginner folk guitar accompaniment. This is a pet project of mine, even though guitar instruction should not live by book alone. The fact is, though, that many people give up studying any music at all because it is taught too often with all the pedagogical stringencies of the potential professional. I have aimed my instruction for the avowed amateur on the simplest possible level. You can go on from there. I hope you do.

Tom Glazer

Scarborough, New York

A New
Treasury of Folk Songs

Acres of Clams

(The Old Settler's Song)

Sometimes called "The Old Settler's Song," this tune is found elsewhere with other lyrics, such as "Old Rosin the Beau."

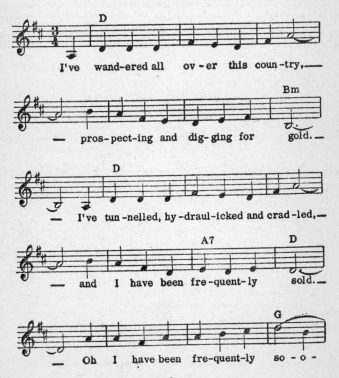

I've wand-ered all ov-er this coun-try,—

— pros-pect-ing and dig-ging for gold.—

— I've tun-nelled, hy-draul-icked and crad-led,—

— and I have been fre-quent-ly sold.—

— Oh I have been fre-quent-ly so-o-

2

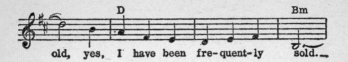

old, yes, I have been fre-quent-ly sold.—

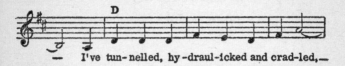

— I've tun-nelled, hy-draul-icked and crad-led,—

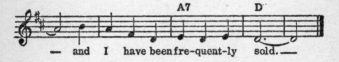

— and I have been fre-quent-ly sold.—

2. For one who gets riches by mining
   Perceiving that hundreds grow poor
   I made up my mind to try farming
   The only pursuit that is sure.
   The only pursuit that is su-u-ure, etc.

3. So rolling my grub in my blanket
   I left all my tools on the ground
   And started one morning to shank it
   For a country they call Puget Sound.
   For a country they call Puget Sou-ou-ound, etc.

4. I tried to get out of the country
   But poverty forced me to stay
   Until I became an old settler
   Now you couldn't drive me away.
   Now you couldn't drive me away-ay-ay, etc.

5. No longer the slave of ambition
   I laugh at the world and its shams
   I think of my happy condition
   Soooo-rounded by acres of clams.
   Soooo-rounded by acres of cla-a-ams, etc.

Barbara Allen

Enough versions have been collected in this country alone to take care of over a hundred Barbara Allens, not to mention those from Scandinavia to Italy.

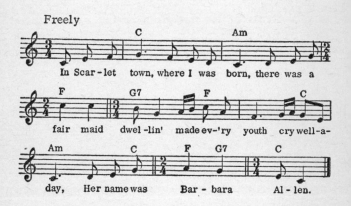

Freely

In Scar-let town, where I was born, there was a fair maid dwel-lin' made ev-'ry youth cry well-a-day, Her name was Bar - bara Al - len.

2. 'Twas in the merry month of May
   The green buds they were swellin'
   Sweet William on his death-bed lay
   For the sake of Bar'bra Allen.

3. He sent his servant to her house
   The place where she was dwellin'
   Said, "You must come to my master's house,
   If your name be Bar'bra Allen."

4. A dying man, O look at me
   One kiss from you will cure me
   One kiss from me, you shall never get
   While your poor heart is breaking.

5. As she was walking down the fields
   She heard some birds a-singing
   And as they sang, they seemed to say,
   "Hard-hearted Bar'bra Allen."

6. Come Mother, come, make up my bed
   Make it both long and narrow
   My true love died for me yesterday
   I'll die for him tomorrow.

7. And he was buried in Edmundstone
   And she was buried in Cold Harbour
   And out of him grew roses red
   And out of her green brier.

8. They grew and grew so very high
   Till they could grow no higher
   And at the top grew a true lover's knot
   And around it twined green brier.

The Bennington Rifles

During the Revolutionary War, General John Burgoyne made a disastrous march from Canada down to Albany. Near Bennington, Vermont, one of his detachments was routed by some ragtag and bobtail American troops. A handsome monument marks the spot, and this song the occasion.

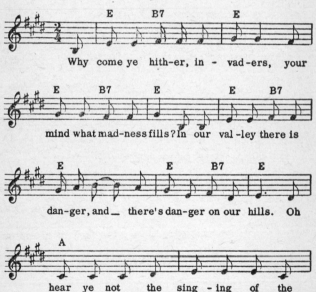

Why come ye hith-er, in - vad-ers, your mind what mad-ness fills? In our val-ley there is dan-ger, and _ there's dan-ger on our hills. Oh hear ye not the sing-ing of the bug-le proud and free. Full soon you'll hear the

6

For the rifle (clap, clap) the rifle — (clap, clap) In our hands will prove no trifle —— — yes, the rifle — (clap, clap) the rifle — (clap, clap) In our hands will prove no trifle. ——

2. Ye ride a goodly steed; ye may know another master
   Ye hither come with speed, but ye'll learn to back much faster
   When you meet our mountain boys and their leader, Johnny Stark
   They're lads who make but little noise and always hit the mark.
   For the rifle, the rifle, etc.

3. Have ye no graves at home, across the briny water
   That hither ye must come like a bullock to the slaughter
   If we the job must do, then the sooner 'tis begun
   If flint and trigger hold but true the quicker 'twill be won.
   For the rifle, etc.

Black Is the Color

John Jacob Niles' happiest arrangement of his happiest collector's items.

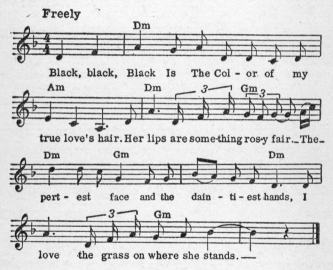

2. I love my love and well she knows
   I love the grass whereon she goes
   If she on earth no more I see
   My life will quickly leave me.

3. I go to Troublesome to mourn to weep
   But satisfied I ne'er can sleep
   I'll write her a note in a few little lines
   I'll suffer death a thousand times.

4. Repeat first verse.

Blow the Candles Out

I picked up this lovely apprentice song in Washington, D.C., in 1942. It had hitherto been unprinted and uncollected.

When I was ap-pren-ticed in Lon - don, I went to see my dear, __ The cand-les were_all burn - ing, the moon shone bright and clear. I knocked at her win-dow to ease her of her pain. She rose to let __ me in, Then she barred the doors a - gain.

2. I like your well-behavior, and thus I often say
   I cannot rest contented, whilst you are gone away
   The roads they are so muddy, we cannot gang about
   Come roll me in your arms, love, and blow the candles out.

3. Your father and your mother in yonder room doth lie
   A-huggin' one another, so why not you and I
   A-huggin' one another, without a fear or doubt
   Come roll me in your arms, dear, and blow the candles
       out.

4. And if you prove successful, love, pray name him after me,
   Keep him neat and kiss him sweet, and bounce him on
       your knee
   When my three years are ended, my time it will be out
   Then I will double my indebtedness, by blowing the can-
       dles out.

Blow the Man Down

The word "blow" here means "knock," and Paradise Street was in the disreputable section of town. There were four main types of sea chanteys: short-drag, for shorter jobs; halyard, for longer and heavier jobs such as hoisting sail; capstan, a barrel-like object with bars which the men grasped and worked by walking around and around; and fo'c'stle chanteys, which were sung on their off periods. This one is a halyard chantey.

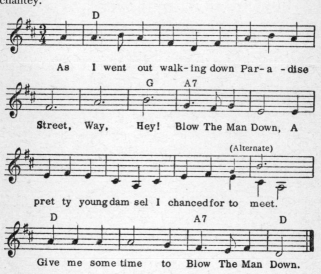

As I went out walk-ing down Par-a -dise Street, Way, Hey! Blow The Man Down, A pret ty young dam sel I chanced for to meet. (Alternate) Give me some time to Blow The Man Down.

Chorus (*same tune as verses*)

Blow the man down, bullies, blow the man down
To me way, hey, blow the man down
Blow the man down, bullies, blow the man down
Give me some time to blow the man down.

(*The chorus can come as often or as seldom between the verses as one wishes.*)

2. She was round in the counter and bluff in the bow
   To me way, hey, etc.
   So I took in all sails and cried way enough now
   Give me some time, etc.

3. I hailed her in English, she answered me clear
   To me, etc.
   I'm from the Black Arrow bound for the Shakespeare
   Give me some time, etc.

4. So I tailed her my flipper and took her in tow
   To me way, hey
   And yardarm to yardarm away we did go
   Give me some time, etc.

5. But as we were walking she said unto me
   To me, etc.
   There's a spanking full rigger all ready for sea
   Give me some time, etc.

6. The spanking full rigger for New York was bound . . .
   She was very well manned and very well found . . .

7. But as soon as that packet was clear of the bar . . .
   The mate knocked me down with the end of a spar . . .

8. So I give you fair warning before you belay . . .
   Don't ever take heed of what pretty gals say . . .

Blow Ye Winds of the Morning

New Bedford, Massachusetts, in its day, was the chief whaling port of the world. This chantey is a fo'c'stle chantey and one of the best sea songs of all seas, everywhere.

'Tis ad-ver-tised in Bos-ton, New York, and Buf-fa-lo. Five hun-dred brave Am-er-i-cans a-whal-ing for to go sing-in'

CHORUS

Blow ye winds of the morn-ing. Blow ye winds hi-ho, Then clear a way the run nin' gear, and blow, blow, blow.

2. They send you to New Bedford town, that famous whaling port
And hand you to some landsharks there, to board and fit you out, singing . . .

Chorus

3. They send you to a boarding house, there for a time to dwell
   The thieves are there much thicker than the other side of hell, singing

   Chorus

4. They tell you of the clipper-ships, a-going in and out
   And say you'll take five hundred sperm before you're six months out, singing . . .

   Chorus

5. It's now we're out to sea, my boys, the wind comes on to blow
   One half the watch is sick on deck, the other half's below, singing . . .

   Chorus

6. But as for the provisions, boys, we don't get half enough
   A little piece of stinking beef and a damned small bag of duff, singing

   Chorus

7. The skipper's on the quarter-deck a-squintin' at the sails
   When up aloft the lookout sights a heaving school of whales

   Chorus

8. Now clear away the boats, my boys, and after him you'll travel
   And if you get too near his fluke, he'll kick you to the devil

   Chorus

9. When we get home, our ship made fast, and we get thru our sailin'
   A winding glass around we'll pass and damn this blubber whalin', singing

   Chorus

The Blue-Tail Fly

(Jimmie Crack Corn)

Sometimes known as a folk version of a Dan Emmett minstrel
song; but Emmett's song, I am sure, was in turn based on
Negro folk sources, like so many minstrel songs.

VERSE: Freely
CHORUS: Rhythm

When I was young, I uséd to wait up -

on old Mas - ter, and pass his plate, and

fetch the bot-tle when he got dry, And

brush a - way the blue - tail fly.

CHORUS

Jim - mie Crack Corn, and

15

I don't care, Jim-mie Crack Corn, and
I don't care, Jim-mie Crack Corn, and
I don't care. My mas-ter's gone a-way.

2. And when he'd ride in the afternoon
   I'd follow with a hickory broom
   The pony being very shy
   Got bitten by a blue-tail fly.
   Jimmie crack corn . . . etc.

3. One day he rode around the farm
   The flies so numerous they did swarm
   One chanced to bite him on the thigh
   The devil take the blue-tail fly.
   Jimmie crack corn . . . etc.

4. The pony run, he jump, he pitch
   He threw old master in a ditch
   He died and the jury wondered why
   The verdict was the blue-tail fly.
   Jimmie crack corn . . . etc.

5. They laid him under a 'simmon tree
   His epitaph is there to see:
   "Beneath this stone I'm forced to lie
   A victim of the blue-tail fly."
   Jimmie crack corn . . . etc.

2. We went riding one afternoon
   I followed with a hickory broom
   The pony being very shy
   Got bitten by a blue-tail fly.

   Chorus

3. The pony he did rear and pitch
   He threw old master in a ditch
   The jury asked the reason why—
   The verdict was the blue-tail fly.

   Chorus

4. We laid old master down to rest
   And on a stone this last request
   "Beneath the earth, I'm forced to lie
   A victim of the blue-tail fly."

   Chorus

Careless Love

People who derive satisfaction from tracing the origins of certain songs claim this to be one of the earliest of all the blues. Its contours indicate a white origin but that isn't certain. It will last as long as couples love unequally.

Love, oh love, oh Care-less Love.____

Love, oh love, oh Care-less Love.____

Love, oh love, oh Care- less Love.

See what care-less love can do.____

2. I love my mama and my papa, too (*3 times*)
    But I'd leave them both to go with you.

3. Once I wore my apron low (*3 times*)
    Couldn't hardly keep you from my door.

4. Now my apron strings won't pin (*3 times*)
    You pass me by but you won't come in.

5. Repeat first verse.

Cindy

A great example of a "banjo" tune, that is, one which was originally more important than the lyric, being played mainly on America's only native instrument, the banjo. Some years ago, I was singing on a soap opera on radio, and a postcard was sent in asking the network to ". . . get that bango player off the air . . ." It was a catarrh, sir, not a bango.

Have you seen my Cind - y?

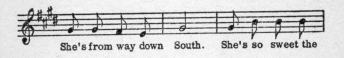

She's from way down South. She's so sweet the

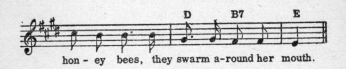

hon - ey bees, they swarm a-round her mouth.

CHORUS

Get-a -long home, Cind-y, Cind-y, Get a-long

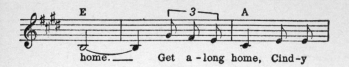

home._____ Get a-long home, Cind-y

Cind-y. I'll mar-ry you some day.

2. I wish I was an apple, hangin' on a tree
   And every time my Cindy'd pass
   She'd take a little bite of me.

   Chorus

3. I wish I was a needle, as fine as I could sew
   I'd sew myself to the girls' coattails
   And down the road I'd go.

   Chorus

4. She took me in her parlor
   She cooled me with her fan
   She said I was the sweetest thing
   In the shape of a mortal man.

   Chorus

5. Cindy got religion
   I'll tell you what she done
   She walked up to the preacher
   And she chawed her chewin' gum.

   Chorus

6. When Cindy got religion
   She went preachin' round the town
   She got so full of glory
   That her stockings they come down.

   Chorus

Colorado Trail

A song in whose deceptive simplicity lies a complex of profound human emotion and beauty.

Freely or rhythm

Eyes like a morn - ing star,

Cheeks like a rose. An - nie was a

prett - ty girl. God al - might - y knows.

Weep all ye lit - tle rains

Wail winds_ wail all a -long, a-

long, a - long the Col - or - a - do Trail.

Cotton-Eyed Joe

The kind of folk song which hints at more than it tells. This is a mournful version of the same Joe found in square-dance or "breakdown" songs.

Freely

Where did you come from? Where do you go? Where do you come from, Cot-ton-Eyed— Joe?

2. Come for to see you.
Come for to sing.
Come for to show you
My diamond ring.

Crawdad

A crawdad, or crayfish, is a crustacean, like a lobster, found in about as many places in the South as there are versions of this song; in fact, there may be more versions than crawdads, at that.

Sit - tin' on the ice till my feet get cold, hon-ey. Sit-tin' on the ice, till my feet get cold, bab-y. Sit - tin' on the ice, till my

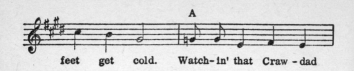

feet get cold. Watch-in' that Craw-dad

in his hole___ hon-ey

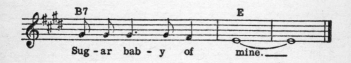

Sug-ar bab-y of mine.___

2. Crawdad, crawdad, you'd better dig deep, honey
   Crawdad, crawdad, you'd better dig deep, baby
   Crawdad, crawdad, you'd better dig deep
   I'm a-gonna ramble in my sleep, honey, sugar-baby of
       mine.

3. Sittin' on the ice till my feet get hot ... *as above*
   Watchin' that crawdad rock and trot ... *as above*

4. Crawdad, crawdad, better go to your hole
   If I don't git you, durn my soul ...

5. Sittin' on the ice till my feet get numb
   Watchin' that crawdad go and come ...

The Dodger

"We're all a-dodging out away through the world." This unusual song is said to have originated in the 1880s, and is as American as corn pone.

Oh, the can - di - date's a Dodg- er, a

well - known Dodg - er, The

can - di - date's a Dodg - er, and

I'm a Dodg - er too. He'll

meet you and treat you and

ask you for your vote, But

look out, boys, he's a-dodg-in' for your note.

CHORUS

We're all a-dodg-in'

dodg-in', dodg-in', dodg-in', We're

all a-dodg-in' out a-way through the world.

2. Yes, the lawyer he's a dodger, a well-known dodger
   Yes, the lawyer, he's a dodger, and I'm a dodger, too
   He'll plead your case and claim you for a friend
   But look out, boys, he's easy for to bend.

   Chorus

3. Yes, the doctor, he's a dodger, a well-known dodger
   The doctor he's a dodger, and I'm a dodger, too
   He'll doctor you and cure you for half you possess
   But look out, boys, he's a-dodging for the rest.

   Chorus

4. Oh the preacher he's a dodger, a well-known dodger
   The preacher, he's a dodger, and I'm a dodger, too
   He'll preach you gospel, and tell you of your crimes
   But look out, boys, he's a-dodging for your dimes.

   Chorus

5. Oh the merchant he's a dodger, a well-known dodger
      well-known dodger
   The merchant, he's a dodger, and I'm a dodger, too
   He'll sell you goods at double the price
   And when you go to pay him you got to pay him twice.

   Chorus

6. Oh the farmer he's a dodger, a well-known dodger
   The farmer, he's a dodger, and I'm a dodger, too
   He'll plow his cotton, he'll plow his corn
   And he'll never make a living just as sure as you're born.

   Chorus

7. Oh the lover he's a dodger, and a well-known dodger
   The lover he's a dodger and I'm a dodger, too
   He'll hug you and kiss you and call you his bride
   But look out, girls, he's telling you a lie.

   Chorus

Down in the Valley

This would have to be considered as one of the five prettiest American folk songs ever. In the 1930s it became a hit in a commercial, juke box version, but it will survive that version, or per-version.

Down In The Val - ley, the val -ley so low. ___ Hang your head o - ver, Hear the wind blow. ___

CHORUS

Hear the wind blow, dear, Hear the wind blow. ___ Hang your head o - ver. Hear the wind blow. ___

2. If you don't love me, love whom you please
   Throw your arms 'round me; give my heart ease
   Give my heart ease, dear, give my heart ease
   Throw your arms 'round me; give my heart ease.

3. Build me a castle, forty feet high
   So I can see you as you go by
   As you go by, dear, etc.

4. Write me a letter; send it by mail
   Send it in care of Birmingham jail.
   Birmingham jail, dear, etc.

5. Roses love sunshine; violets love dew
   Angels in heaven know I love you
   Know I love you, dear, etc.

Drill Ye Tarriers

I had always thought along with many others that "tarriers" was Irish for "terriers," a name given to the early Irish-American railroad workers—or loafers—because of their beards. Recently, though, an Irish-American friend assured me that tarriers simply means, "those who tarry." The Eastern Irishmen were being urged to outdo the Western Chinese railroad workers during the building of the first transcontinental railroad in the late 1860s. Here is one song of which we know the authors' names, to wit, Casey and Connolly.

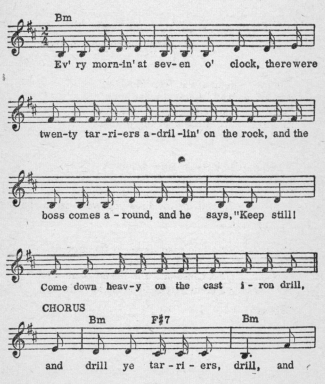

Ev' ry morn-in' at sev-en o' clock, there were twen-ty tar-ri-ers a-dril-lin' on the rock, and the boss comes a-round, and he says, "Keep still! Come down heav-y on the cast i-ron drill,

CHORUS

and drill ye tar-ri-ers, drill, and

drill ye tar-ri-ers, drill. For it's work all day for

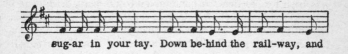

sug-ar in your tay. Down be-hind the rail-way, and

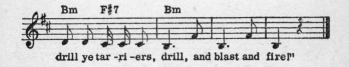

drill ye tar-ri-ers, drill, and blast and fire!"

2. The new foreman was Jean McCann
   By God he was a blamed mean man
   Last week a premature blast went off
   And a mile in the air went big Jim Goff.

   Chorus

3. When next payday it come around
   Jim Goff a dollar short was found
   When he asked what for, came this reply:
   "You were docked for the time you were up in the sky!"

   Chorus

4. The cook was a fine man down to the ground
   He married a lady six foot around
   She baked good cakes and she baked them well
   But she baked them harder than the holes in hell.

   Chorus

The Drunken Sailor

Burl Ives says that on the chorus of this song, a capstan chantey, the men would stomp loudly on the deck.

What shall you do with a Drun-ken Sail-or?

What shall you do with a Drun-ken Sail-or?

What shall you do with a Drun-ken Sail-or

ear-lye in the morn - ing?

CHORUS

Hoo - ray and up she ris-es

Hoo - ray and up she ris-es

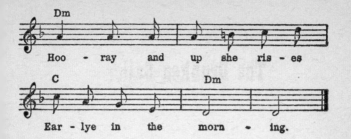

Hoo - ray and up she ris - es

Ear - lye in the morn - ing.

2. Put him in the longboat and wet him all over (*3 times*)
   Earlye in the morning.

   Chorus

3. Put him on the clothes-line with a clothes-pin on him
   (*3 times*)
   Earlye in the morning.

   Chorus

4. Put him in the brig until he's sober

5. Haul him aboard with a running bowline

6. *Repeat first verse*

The E-ri-e

Probably the best known "Canal" song today.

We were fort-y miles from Al-ban-y, For-get it I nev-er shall. What a ter-ri-ble storm we had one night, on the E-ri-e Can-al.

CHORUS

Oh, the E-ri-e was a-

ris - in'___ And the gin was a get - tin'
low, And I scarce - ly think we'll
get a drink, Till we get to Buf - fa -
lo.___ Till we get to Buf - fa - lo.

2. We were chock up full of barley
   We were chock up full of rye
   And the captain he looked down at me
   With his goldurned wicked eye.

   Chorus

3. Now the cook was a fine old lady
   She wore a raggedy dress
   When the winds blew strong, we hist her up
   As a signal of distress.

   Chorus

4. The girls are in the Police Gazette
   The crew is all in jail
   And I'm the only son-of-a-gun
   That's left to tell the tale.

   Chorus

Every Night When the Sun Goes Down

There are many folk songs which are exactly like spirituals except that the lyric is not a religious one. Such is this, from the South, of course.

Freely

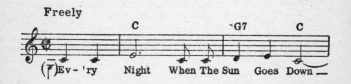

(I) Ev - 'ry Night When The Sun Goes Down —

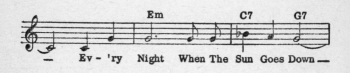

— Ev - 'ry Night When The Sun Goes Down —

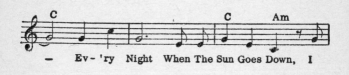

— Ev - 'ry Night When The Sun Goes Down,   I

hang down my head, — And mourn - ful   cry. —

Chorus: (*same tune as verse*)

True love, don't weep, true love, don't mourn
True love, don't weep, true love, don't mourn
True love, don't weep or mourn for me,
I'm going away to Marbletown.

2. I wish to the Lord my train would come (*3 times*)
   And take me back where I come from.

   Chorus

3. I wish to the Lord my babe was born
   A-sitting on his pappy's knee
   And I, poor girl, was dead and gone,
   And the green grass growing over me.

   Chorus

Fare Thee Well, O Honey

A classic statement in simple, deeply felt, terms. The lyric
has been favorably compared to Sappho by Carl Sandburg.

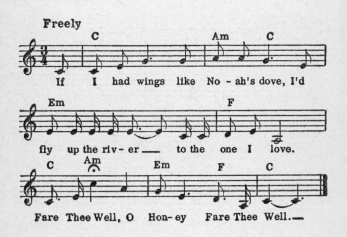

If I had wings like No-ah's dove, I'd
fly up the riv-er ___ to the one I love.
Fare Thee Well, O Hon-ey Fare Thee Well.___

2. If I had listened to what my mamma said
   I'd still be sleepin' near my mamma's bed.
   Fare thee well, O honey, fare thee well.

3. I got a man, he's long and tall
   He moves his body like a cannon ball.
   Fare thee well, O honey, fare thee well.

4. One of these days, and it won't be long
   You're gonna hear my name, but I'll be gone.
   Fare thee well, O honey, fare thee well.

The Farmer

A fragment of this song was heard in the early 1890s, but it has been traced as far back as just after the Civil War.

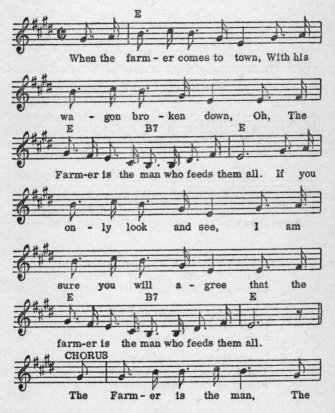

When the farm-er comes to town, With his wa-gon bro-ken down, Oh, The Farm-er is the man who feeds them all. If you on-ly look and see, I am sure you will a-gree that the farm-er is the man who feeds them all.

CHORUS

The Farm-er is the man, The

Farm - er is the man.

Lives on cred-it till the fall. Then they

take him by the hand and they

lead him from the land, and the

cred-i -tor's the man who gets it all.

2. When the lawyer hangs around, while the butcher cuts a
      pound
   Oh the farmer is the man who feeds them all
   And the preacher and the cook, they go strolling by the
      brook
   But the farmer is the man who feeds them all.

   Chorus

3. When the banker says he's broke, and the merchant's up
      in smoke
   They forget that it's the farmer feeds them all
   It would put them to the test, if the farmer took a rest
   Then they'd know that it's the farmer feeds them all.

   Chorus

The Farmer's Cursed Wife

There are many versions of this Anglo-American song; I learned this one from Richard Dyer-Bennet's singing.

Two-beat rhythm

A farm-er was plough-ing his field one day. Right-ful, right-ful, id-dy fie-day. A farm-er was plough-ing his field one day, when the dev-il came to him, and to him did say, "With my right-fal-lal-id-dy fie-day, right-ful, right-ful id-dy fie-day.

2. See here, my good man, I have come for your wife
   Rightful, rightful, iddy fie day
   See here, my good man, I have come for your wife
   For she's the bane and torment of your life
   With my right fa lal, iddy fie day
   Rightful, rightful, iddy fie day

3. So the devil histed her up on his hump
   Rightful, etc.
   The devil he histed her up on his hump
   And down to hell with her he did jump
   With my right fa lal, etc.

4. But when they got there the gates they were shut
   Rightful, etc.
   When they got there the gates they were shut
   With a sweep of her arm she laid open his nut
   With my right fa lal, etc.

5. Six little devils sat on the wall
   Rightful, etc.
   Six little devils sat on the wall
   Said take her back daddy, she'll murder us all
   With my right fa lal, etc.

6. So the devil he histed her back on his hump
   Rightful, etc.
   The devil he histed her back on his hump
   And back to earth with her he did jump
   With my right fa lal, etc.

7. See here, my good man, I've come back with your wife
   Rightful, etc.
   See here, my good man, I've come back with your wife
   For she's the bane and torment of my life
   With my right fa lal, etc.

8. Now they say that the women are worst than the men
   Rightful, etc.
   They say that the women are worst than the men
   They got sent down to hell and kicked out again
   With my right fa lal, etc.

The Fireship

A beautiful broth of a bawdy ballad, disarming enough to overcome the most reticent.

VERSE: Freely
CHORUS: Rhythm

As I walked out one eve-en-ing up-on my night's car-eer, I spied a pret-ty Fire-ship and to her I did steer. I hoist-ed up my sig-nal which she did quick-ly view.— And when I had my bunt-ing up, she immed-iate-ly hove to.—

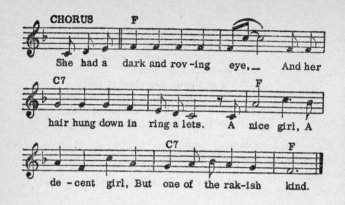

CHORUS

She had a dark and rov-ing eye, ___ And her hair hung down in ring a lets. A nice girl, A de - cent girl, But one of the rak-ish kind.

2. Excuse me, sir, she said to me
   For being out so late
   For if my parents knew of this
   Then sad would be my fate
   My father was a minister
   A good and virtuous man
   My mother is a Methodist
   I do the best I can . . .

   Chorus

3. I took her to a tav-er-in
   And treated her with wine
   O little did I ever think
   She was the rakish kind
   I handled her, I dandled her
   But much to my surprise
   She was only an old pirate ship
   Rigged up in a disguise . . .

   Chorus

4. So listen all you sailormen
   Who sail upon the sea
   Beware of them there fireships
   One was the ruin of me
   Beware of them, stay clear of them
   They'll be the death of you
   'Twas there I had my mizzen sprung
   And my strong-box broken through . . .

   Chorus

The Foggy Dew

Burl Ives may not remember this incident. One night at the now defunct night club, Cafe Society Uptown, where he was appearing, he mentioned to me that the censors of his network program were forbidding him to sing "The Foggy Dew," because the last verse implied that the hero of the song was unmarried. ("And now I am a bachelor/I live with my son....") I told Burl that I had encountered similar difficulties and had got around them by changing the line to "*Again*, I am a bachelor..." to imply a former marriage.

VERSE: Freely
CHORUS: Rhythm

Once I was a bach-'lor, I lived all a-lone, I worked at the weav-er's trade____ and the on-ly, on-ly, thing I did that was wrong was to woo a fair young maid.____

CHORUS
I wooed her in the sum-mer-

time, And part of the win - ter too. _____ And the on - ly, on - ly, thing I did that was wrong, was to shield her from the Fog - gy, Fog - gy Dew. ____

2. One night she crept close by my side
   As I lay down to sleep
   The moonlight glistened on her pale face
   As she began to weep
   She wept, she cried, she tore her hair
   Ah me, what could I do
   And all night long, I held her in my arms
   Just to shield her from the foggy, foggy dew.

3. Again I am a bachelor, I live with my son
   We work at the weaver's trade
   And every, every time, I look into his eyes
   He reminds me of the fair young maid
   He reminds me of the summer time
   And part of the winter, too
   And the many, many times, I held her in my arms
   Just to shield her from the foggy, foggy dew.

Frankie and Johnnie

One of the great classic American ballads. Its origins, after much investigation, are lost in the mists of the past. Some claim to have heard the song before 1850. There are, of course, many, many versions. Frankie is the woman in all the versions but Johnnie, the man's name, is sometimes Albert or many other names.

"Bluesy"

Fran – kie and John nie were lov – ers___
Oh, Lord y, How__ they could love. They
swore to be true to each oth – er___
True as the stars a – bove. He was her
man.___ And he done her wrong.__

Frankie and Johnnie went walking
Johnnie in his brand new suit
Said Frankie to Johnnie, "O Lordy
Don't my Johnnie-man look cute?"
He was her man, and he done her wrong.

Johnnie said, "I've got to leave you
But I won't be very long
Don't wait up for me, Honey
Or worry while I'm gone."
He was her man, and he was doin' her wrong.

Frankie went down to the corner
Went in the saloon for some beer
She said to the fat bartender,
"Has my Johnnie-man been here?"
He was her man, and he done her wrong.

"Well, I won't tell you no story
And I won't tell you no lie
I saw your Johnnie 'bout an hour ago
With a gal named Nellie Bly.
If he's your man, he's doin' you wrong."

Oh, Frankie got off at South Twelfth Street
Looked up in a window so high
And there she saw her Johnnie
A-huggin' that Nellie Bly;
He was her man, and he was doin' her wrong.

Frankie pulled out her six-shooter
Pulled out her old forty-four
Her gun went rooty-toot-toot-toot
And Johnnie rolled over the floor;
He was her man, and he done her wrong.

"Oh, roll me over so easy
Oh, roll me over so slow
Oh, roll me over easy, boys
For my wounds they hurt me so;
I was her man, and I done her wrong."

Frankie got down on her knees
Took Johnnie into her lap
She started to hug and kiss him
But there was no bringing him back;
He was her man, and he done her wrong.

"Oh, get me a thousand policemen
Oh, throw me into your cell
'Cause I've shot my Johnnie so dead
I know I'm goin' to hell;
Though he was my man, and he done me wrong."

Roll out your rubber-tired carriage
Oh, roll out your old-time hack
There's twelve men goin' to the graveyard
And eleven coming back;
He was her man, and he done her wrong.

The Frog Went A-Courtin'

This is the kind of song whose many versions each have their adherents. I adhere to this one, but I like them all.

The   Frog went a court-in', He did ride, H'm,

H'm,   H'm, H'm   The Frog went a court-in'

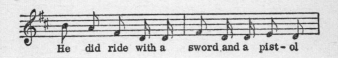

He   did ride with a   sword and a   pist-ol

by his side, H'm, H'm,   H'm, H'm.

2. He rode up to Miss Mousie's den, h'm, h'm; h'm, h'm
   He rode up to Miss Mousie's den
   Said, "Please, Miss Mousie, won't you let me in, h'm, h'm;
   h'm, h'm.

3. "First I must ask, my Uncle Rat
   And see what he will say to that . . . etc.

4. Miss Mousie, dear, won't you marry me, h'm, h'm; etc.
   Miss Mousie, dear, won't you marry me
   Way down under the apple tree, etc.

5. Where will the wedding supper be, etc.
   Where will the wedding supper be
   Under the same old apple tree . . . etc.

6. What will the wedding supper be . . . etc.
   What will the wedding supper be
   Hominy grits and a black-eyed pea . . . etc.

7. The first come in was a bumble bee, bz-z-z, b-z-z; b-z-z,
   b-z-z
   The first come in was a bumble bee
   With a big bass fiddle on his knee, b-z-z, b-z-z; b-z-z,
   b-z-z.

8. The last come in was a mocking bird, mock, mock; mock,
   mock
   The last come in was a mocking bird
   And said this marriage is too absurd, mock, mock; mock,
   mock.

Git Along Little Dogies

(Whoopee Ti-Yi-Yo)

This one has my vote as the best of the cowboy songs.

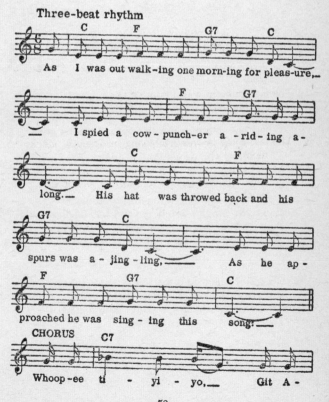

Three-beat rhythm

As I was out walk-ing one morn-ing for pleas-ure, I spied a cow-punch-er a-rid-ing a-long. His hat was throwed back and his spurs was a-jing-ling, As he ap-proached he was sing-ing this song:

CHORUS

Whoop-ee ti-yi-yo, Git A-

long Lit-tle Dog-ies,___ It's your mis-

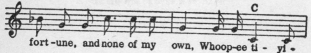

fort-une, and none of my own, Whoop-ee ti - yi -

yo, Git A-long Lit-tle Dog-ies, you know that Wy-

om-ing will be your new home.___

2. Your mother was raised way down in Texas
   Where the jimson weed and the sand-burrs grow
   We'll fill you up on prickly pear and cholla
   Then throw you on the trail to Idaho.

   Chorus

3. Early in the spring we round up the dogies
   We mark 'em and brand 'em and bob off their tails
   Round up the horses, load up the chuck-wagon
   Then throw the dogies out on the long trail.

   Chorus

4. Oh you'll make soup for Uncle Sam's Injuns
   It's "Beef, heap beef" I hear them cry
   Git along, git along, git along, little dogies
   You'll be big steers by and by.

   Chorus

Go Down, Moses

The great spiritual.

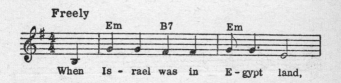

When Is - rael was in E - gypt land,

Let my peo ple go, Op - pressed so hard they

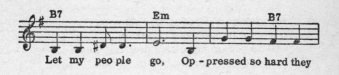

could not stand, let my peo-ple go.

Go Down Mo - ses, way down in

E- gypt land,___ tell _ ole ___

Phar-oah,__ to let my peo-ple go.

2. Thus saith the Lord, bold Moses said
   Let my people go
   If not I'll smite your first-born dead
   Let my people go.

   Chorus

3. No more shall they in bondage toil, etc.
   Let them come out with Egypt's spoil, etc.

   Chorus

4. We need not always weep and mourn, etc.
   And wear those slavery's chains forlorn, etc.

   Chorus

5. The devil thought he had us fast, etc.
   But we thought we'd break his chains at last, etc.

   Chorus

Go Tell Aunt Rhody

Aunt Rhody is at times Nancy, or other names. This song might be called an answer to the song, "The Gray Goose," which see.

Go Tell Aunt Rhod - y, Go
Tell Aunt Rhod - y, Go Tell Aunt Rhod -
y, the old gray goose is dead.

2. The one we've been saving (*3 times*)
   To make a feather-bed.

3. She died on Friday (*3 times*)
   With an aching in her head.

4. Old gander's weeping (*3 times*)
   Because his wife is dead.

5. Goslings are mourning (*3 times*)
   Because their mother's dead.

6. *Repeat first verse.*

Goin' Down the Road

This must have been a prison song, to judge by the words, though I don't think it ever was collected in a prison. Do we like prison songs so much because we are all in prisons one way or the other? Or do we sympathize unconsciously with criminals, since ". . . we all have a little larceny in our hearts . . ."

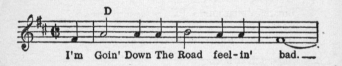

I'm Goin' Down The Road feel-in' bad. ___

___ I'm Goin' Down The Road feel-in' bad, ___ I'm

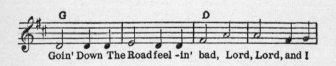

Goin' Down The Road feel-in' bad, Lord, Lord, and I

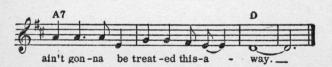

ain't gon-na be treat-ed this-a - way. ___

2. I'm down in the jail on my knees (*3 times*)
   Lord, Lord,
   And I ain't gonna be treated this-a-way.

3. They feed me on corn-bread and cheese (*3 times*)
   Lord, Lord,
   And I ain't gonna be treated this-a-way.

4. I'm goin' where my clothing suits the clime (*3 times*)
   Lord, Lord,
   And I ain't gonna be treated this-a-way.

5. I'm goin' where the water tastes like wine (*3 times*)
   Lord, Lord,
   And I ain't gonna be treated this-a-way.

6. Two dollar shoes hurts my feet (*3 times*)
   Lord, Lord,
   And I ain't gonna be treated this-a-way.

7. But ten dollar shoes fits 'em neat (*3 times*)
   Lord, Lord,
   And I ain't gonna be treated this-a-way.

8. *Repeat first verse.*

Got an Old Mule

(Low Bridge, Everybody Down)

Carl Carmer, the famous folklorist, tells that the mule drivers on the Erie Canal would shout out, "Low bridge, everybody down!" and many a rider would get a bruised noggin from failing to pay attention.

I Got An Old Mule, and her name is Sal,

Fif - teen years on the E - rie Can - al,
(miles)

She's a good work er, and a good old pal,

Fif - teen years on the E - rie Can - al, We've
(miles)

hauled some bar - ges in our day,

Full of lum - ber, coal and hay, And

60

2. We better get along on our way, old gal
   Fifteen miles on the Erie Canal
   Cause you bet your life I'd never part with Sal
   Fifteen miles on the Erie Canal
   Get up there, mule, here comes a lock
   We'll make Rome 'bout six o'clock
   One more trip and back we'll go
   Right back home to Buffalo.

   Chorus

The Gray Goose

One version of this song was found in a penitentiary, sung by a prisoner who had in turn learned it from another convict who had died in prison.

2. My daddy went a-huntin', Lawd, Lawd, Lawd (*twice*)

3. Well, along come a gray goose, Lawd, Lawd, etc.

4. Throwed the gun to his shoulder, etc.

5. Well, he pulled on the trigger, etc.

6. He was six weeks a-fallin', etc.

7. He was six weeks a-findin', etc.

8. And we put him on the wagon ...

9.   And we took him to the farmhouse . . .

10.   He was six weeks a-pickin' . . .

11.   And we put him on to parboil . . .

12.   He was six months a-parboil . . .

13.   And we put him on the table . . .

14.   Now the forks couldn't stick him . . .

15.   And the knife couldn't cut him . . .

16.   And we throwed him in the hogpen . . .

17.   And he broke the sow's jawbone . . .

18.   And we took him to the sawmill . . .

19.   And he broke the saw's teeth out

20.   And the last time I seed him . . .

21.   He was flyin' cross the ocean . . .

22.   With a long string of goslins . . .

23.   And he's goin', "Quank, quink-quank" . . .

Greensleeves

A song already old in Shakespearean England, it is one of the oldest songs in Western music. In Shakespeare's time it was sung or played fast, not lyrically as today. The same tune is used in the carol "What Child Is This?" There are other verses. I like to sing just this one, for the others get boring, and destroy the mood.

A - las, my love you do me

wrong to treat me so dis -

court - eous - ly. And I have

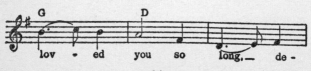

lov - ed you so long, de -

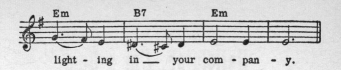

light - ing in — your com - pan - y.

CHORUS

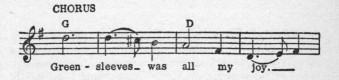

Green - sleeves— was all my joy.—

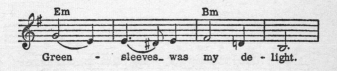

Green - sleeves— was my de - light.

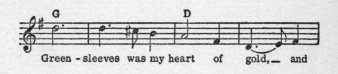

Green - sleeves was my heart of gold,— and

who— but La - dy Green - sleeves?

Hallelujah, I'm a Bum

A parody of a gospel hymn. Some people still swear it is an old Wobbly (International Workers of the World) song. Others disagree—saying that it was found scribbled on the walls of a jail in Kansas City, where an old hobo had been sleeping it off. Now, parodies of the parody exist, one being an anti-Jim Crow song, called "Hallelujah, I'm A-Travelling."

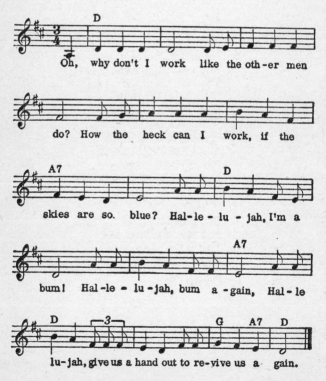

Oh, why don't I work like the oth-er men do? How the heck can I work, if the skies are so blue? Hal-le-lu-jah, I'm a bum! Hal-le-lu-jah, bum a-gain, Hal-le-lu-jah, give us a hand out to re-vive us a gain.

2. When springtime has come
   Oh won't we have fun
   We'll throw up our jobs
   And we'll go on the bum.

   Chorus

3. I went to a house
   And I knocked on the door
   A lady came out, says,
   "You been here before."

   Chorus

4. Oh springtime has come
   And I'm just out of jail
   Ain't got no money
   It all went for bail.

   Chorus

5. I went to a house
   And I asked for some bread
   The lady come out, says,
   "The baker is dead."

   Chorus

6. Went into a saloon
   And I asked for a drink
   They gave me a glass
   And they showed me the sink.

   Chorus

7. Oh, I love my boss
   And my boss loves me
   That is the reason
   I'm so hung-a-ry.

   Chorus

The Hammer Song

A fusion of a powerful tune with lyrics which overtake poetry. The words are addressed sarcastically to the guard of the chain gang, called "Captain," and the interspersed rhythmic grunts echo the hammer strokes striking the implacable rocks.

Take this ham-mer (Huh!) car-ry it to the

cap - tain. (Huh!) Take this ham - mer

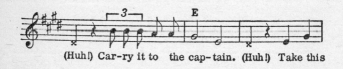

(Huh!) Car-ry it to the cap-tain. (Huh!) Take this

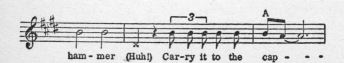

ham - mer (Huh!) Car-ry it to the cap - - -

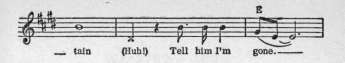

__ tain   (Huh!)   Tell him I'm   gone.____

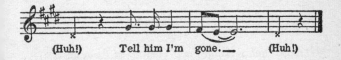

(Huh!)   Tell him I'm   gone.__   (Huh!)

2. If he ask you, (huh!) "Was I runnin'?" (huh!) (*3 times*)
   Tell him I was flyin' (huh!) (*twice*)

3. If he ask you, (huh!) "Was I laughin'?" (huh!) (*as above*)
   Tell him I was cryin', (huh!) (*twice, as above*)

4. I don't want no, (huh!) corn bread 'n molasses (*as above*)
   Hurts my pride, (huh!) (*as above*)

5. *Repeat first verse*

Haul Away, Joe

The most famous "short-drag" chantey of them all.

2. King Louis was the King of France
   Before the Revolution
   Way, haul away, we'll haul away Joe
   But the people chopped his head off
   Which spoiled his constitution
   Way haul away . . .

3. Once I had a Boston girl, but she was fat and lazy
   Way, haul away . . .
   And then I got a New York girl
   She darn near drove my crazy
   Way, haul away . . .

4. Way haul away, we'll haul for better weather
   Way, haul away . . .
   Way haul away, we'll sail away together
   Way, haul away . . .

Henry Martin

An English sea song, sung widely here.

There were three broth-ers in mer-ry Scot-land, in mer-ry Scot-land, there were three. And they did cast lots which of them should go, should go, should go. And turn rob-ber all on the salt sea.

2. The lot it fell first upon Henry Martin
   The youngest of all the three
   That he should turn robber all on the salt sea, the salt
      sea, the salt sea
   For to maintain his two brothers and he.

3. They had not been sailing but a short winter's night
   And part of a short winter's day
   Before they espied a stout lofty ship, lofty ship, lofty ship
   Come abibbing down on them straightway.

4. Hello, hello, cried Henry Martin
   What makes you sail so nigh
   I'm a rich merchant ship bound for fair London town,
       London town, London town
   Will you please for to let me pass by?

5. Oh no, oh no, cried Henry Martin
   That thing it never could be
   For I am turned robber all on the salt sea, the salt sea,
       the salt sea
   For to maintain my two brothers and me.

6. Come lower your tops'l and ring up your mizz'n
   And bring your ship under my lea
   Or I will give you a full flowing ball, flowing ball, flow-
       ing ball
   And your dear bodies drown in the salt sea.

7. Oh no, we won't lower our lofty topsail
   Or bow ourselves under your lea
   And you shan't take from us our rich merchant goods,
       merchant goods, merchant goods
   And you won't drown us all in the salt sea.

8. With broadside and broadside and at it they went
   For fully two hours or three
   Till Henry Martin gave to her the death shot, the death
       shot, the death shot
   And straight to the bottom went she.

9. Bad news, bad news to Old England came
   Bad news to fair London town
   There's a rich merchant ship, and she's sunk in the sea,
       in the sea, in the sea
   And all of her merry men drowned.

He's Got the Whole World

(In His Hand)

A great spiritual which, unaccountably, is not found in the popular folk song collections. It just sort of floated around, the way many folk songs do, until it suddenly burst forth as a popular hit song recently.

1. He's got the little bitty baby in His hand (*3 times*)
   He's got the whole world in His hand.

   Chorus

2. He's got you and me, brother, in His hand (*3 times*)
   He's got the whole world in His hand.

   Chorus

3. He's got you and me, sister, in His hand (*3 times*)
   He's got the whole world in His hand.

   Chorus

4. He's got the little bitty baby, in His hand (*3 times*)
   He's got the whole world in His hand.

   Chorus

Home on the Range

After President Franklin D. Roosevelt allowed as how it was his favorite song in 1933, its popularity created a violent copyright dispute, which ended in the song's being declared to be in the public domain. It was sung in Kansas as early as the 1860s under the title "My Western Home."

Oh give me a home, Where the

buf - fa - lo roam, Where the deer and the

an - te - lope play. Where sel - dom is

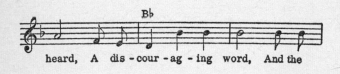

heard, A dis - cour - ag - ing word, And the

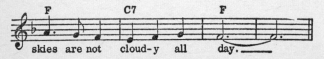

skies are not cloud-y all day.

CHORUS

Home, Home On The Range, — Where the

deer and the an - te - lope play, — Where

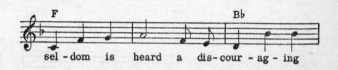

sel - dom is heard a dis - cour - ag - ing

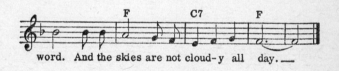

word. And the skies are not cloud - y all day. —

I Know My Love

A fine Irish song, well-known here.

Freely

I know my love, by her way of walk- ing, and I know my love, by her way of talk - ing, And I know my love by her suit of blue, but if my love leaves me, what would I do? _____ And yet she

cries: "I love you the best." But a troub-led mind, sure can know no rest ____ and yet she cries: "Bon-ny boys are few." But if my love loves me, what would I do?

2. There is a dance-hall at Mollakide
   Where my true love goes every night
   And there she sits on some strange lad's knee.
   Well, don't you know now, that vexes me
   And yet she cries, "I love you the best,"
   But a troubled mind, sure can know no rest.
   And yet she cries, "Bonny boys are few,"
   But if my love leaves me, what would I do?

I Know Where I'm Goin'

Another Irish song very popular here. A line went originally: "Some say he's black . . ." black meaning dour, but out of deference to Negro sensitivities most American singers sing the line: "Some say he's dark . . ."

2. I'll wear stockings of silk
   And shoes of bright green leather
   Combs to buckle my hair
   And a ring for every finger.

3. Feather-beds are soft
   And painted rooms are bonny
   But I would trade them all
   For my handsome, winsome Johnny

4. Some say he's dark
   But I say he's bonny
   Fairest of them all
   Is my handsome, winsome, Johnny.

I Ride an Old Paint

No one I know had ever explained what exactly a "hoolihan" is, which the cowboy sings he is going to Montana to throw, until a demon editor at Bantam Books found a definition in *The American Thesaurus of Slang* to which you are cordially referred.

I ride an old paint, I lead an old dam. I'm goin' to Mon-tan-a to throw the hoo-li-han. You feed them in the cou-lees and wa-ter in the draw. Their tails are all mat-ted and backs are all raw.

CHORUS A7

Ride a-round, lit-tle dog-ies, 'ride a-

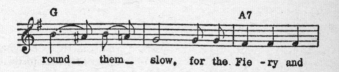

round_ them_ slow, for the Fie-ry and

Snuf-fy are rar-in' to go.

2. Old Bill Jones had a daughter and a son
   His son went to college and the daughter went wrong
   His wife got killed in a free-for-all fight
   Still he keeps a-singin' from morning till night—

   Chorus

3. When I die take my saddle from the wall
   Put it onto my pony, lead him out of the stall
   Tie my bones on his back, turn our faces to the West
   And we'll ride the prairies that we love the best.

   Chorus

4. I've worked in the town, I've worked on the farm
   And all I got to show is the muscle in my arm
   Blisters on my feet and callous on my hand
   I'm goin' to Montana to throw the hoolihan . . .

   Chorus

I'm Gone Away

Sometimes called "He's Gone Away." The mountain referred to, Yandro, is a peak in North Carolina.

I'm Gone A-way, For to stay a lit-tle while, But I'm com-in' back, If I go ten thou-sand miles.__ Oh, who will tie your shoe.__ And who will glove your hand,__ And who will kiss your

rub- y lips when I am gone? Look a

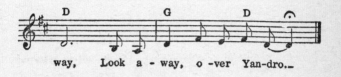

way, Look a - way, o -ver Yan-dro._

2. I'm gone away for to stay a little while
   But I'm comin' back, if I go ten thousand miles
   It's Pappy will tie your shoe
   And Mammy will glove your hand
   And I will kiss your ruby lips
   When I come back
   Look away, look away, over Yandro.

Jennie Jenkins

America abounds in nonsense songs. Europeans wonder why nonsense songs are often written here about crises or disasters. It is our way of bearing up under strain. Jennie Jenkins is now a favorite with children especially.

Will you wear white, oh my dear, oh, my dear?

Will you wear white, Jen-nie Jen - kins?___

— No, I won't wear white, for the

col-or's too bright, I'll buy me a fol-de rol-de-

til - de - tol - de - seek - a - doub- le

Use - a - cause- a - roll   a - find - me -

roll,____ Jen- nie Jen -kins , roll.____

2. Will you wear green, Oh my dear, oh my dear
   Will you wear green, Jennie Jenkins?
   No, I won't wear green; it ain't fit to be seen
   I'll buy me, etc.

3. Will you wear blue . . .
   No I won't wear blue, cause blue won't do . . . etc.

4. Will you wear red . . . etc.
   No, I won't wear red; it's the color of my head . . . etc.

5. Will you wear purple . . . etc.
   No, I won't wear purple; it's the color of a turtle . . . etc.

Jesse James

America's classic Robin Hood legend in song. James was supposed to have been living in St. Louis under the name of Howard when he was shot in the back of his head by his one-time friend, Robert Ford.

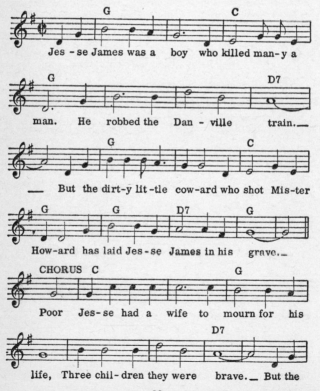

Jes - se James was a boy who killed man-y a man. He robbed the Dan - ville train.__ __ But the dirt-y lit -tle cow-ard who shot Mis-ter How-ard has laid Jes - se James in his grave.__

CHORUS

Poor Jes- se had a wife to mourn for his life, Three chil- dren they were brave.__ But the

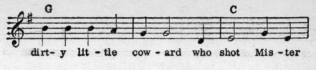

dirt-y lit-tle cow-ard who shot Mis-ter

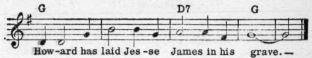

How-ard has laid Jes-se James in his grave.—

2. It was Robert Ford, that dirty little coward,
   I wonder how he does feel
   For he ate of Jesse's bread, and he slept in Jesse's bed
   Then laid poor Jesse in his grave.

   Chorus

3. Jesse was a man, a friend to the poor
   He never would see a man suffer pain,
   And with his brother Frank that robbed the Chicago bank,
   And stopped the Glendale train.

   Chorus

4. It was on a Saturday night, Jesse was at home,
   Talking with his family brave
   Robert Ford came along like a thief in the night
   And laid poor Jesse in his grave.

   Chorus

5. Jesse went to his rest with his hand on his breast
   The devil will be upon his knee
   He was born one day in the county of Clay
   And came from a solitary race.

   Chorus

6. This song was made by Billy Gashade
   As soon as the news did arrive;
   He said there was no man with the law in his hand,
   Who could take Jesse James when alive.

   Chorus

John Henry

The tremendous tale of a tremendous man, the Negro Paul Bunyan, who beat the steam drill and died doing it.

When John Hen - ry___ was a lit - tle ba - by___ Sit - tin' on __ his mam - my's knee, He picked up a ham - mer and a piece of ___ steel, said: "This ham - mer'll be the death __ of ___ me, Lord, Lord, This ham - mer'll be the death __ of ___ me.

2. Well the Captain said to John Henry
   "Gonna bring that steam drill 'round
   Gonna bring that steam drill out on the job
   Gonna whup that steel on down
   Gonna whup that steel on down"

3. John Henry said to the Captain,
   "Bring that thirty pound hammer round
   Thirty pound hammer with a nine foot handle
   Gonna beat your steam drill down
   Gonna beat your steam drill down"

4. John Henry drove about fifteen feet
   The steam drill drove but nine
   He drove so hard that he broke his heart
   And he laid down his hammer and he died
   And he laid down his hammer and he died.

5. John Henry had a little woman
   Her name was Mary Ann
   John Henry took sick and went to bed
   Mary Ann drove steel like a man
   Mary Ann drove steel like a man.

6. John Henry said to his shaker
   "Shaker, why don't you sing
   I'm throwin' thirty pounds from my hips on down
   Just listen to the cold steel ring
   Just listen to the cold steel ring."

7. They took John Henry to the graveyard
   And they buried him in the sand
   And every engine come a-roarin' by,
   Whistled: "There lies a steel-drivin' man
                There lies a steel-drivin' man."

Johnny Has Gone for a Soldier

An American Revolutionary War version of the Irish song, "Shule Aroon." The tune is also found as a sea chantey, a game song, a lumberjack song, et al.

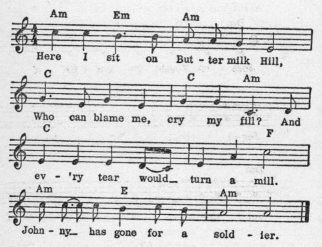

Am   Em   Am

Here I sit on But-ter milk Hill,

C   C   Am

Who can blame me, cry my fill? And

C   F

ev-'ry tear would turn a mill.

Am   E   Am

John-ny has gone for a sold-ier.

2. I'll sell my rod and I'll sell my reel
Like wise I'll sell my spinning wheel
To buy my true love a sword of steel
Johnny has gone for a soldier.

3. Me, O, my, I love him so
Broke my heart to see him go
And only time can heal my woe.
Johnny has gone for a soldier.

4. *Repeat first verse.*

Joshua Fought the Battle of Jericho

A happy spiritual, deservedly one of the most famous.

CHORUS

Josh - ua Fought the Bat - tle of Jer - i - cho,__ Jer - i - cho,__ Jer - i - cho,____ Josh - ua Fought the Bat - tle of Jer - i - cho, And the walls came tumb - ling down.

You can talk a - bout your king of

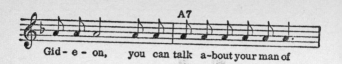

Gid - e - on, you can talk a-bout your man of

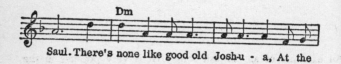

Saul. There's none like good old Josh-u - a, At the

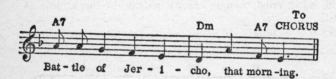

Bat - tle of Jer - i - cho, that morn -ing.

2. Up to the walls of Jericho
   He marched with spear in hand
   "Go blow them horns," old Joshua cried,
   "Cause the battle is in my hand."
   That morning . . .

   Chorus

3. Then the lamb ram horns begin to blow
   Trumpets begin to sound
   Joshua commanded the children to shout
   And the walls came tumbling down . . . that morning . . .

   Chorus

94

The Keeper

An example of an English song that is very popular in the United States, and one which has survived virtually intact with no colonial change, except perhaps in the accents of Americans who love to sing it. At least a second voice is necessary to supply the song's "answers."

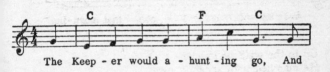

The Keep - er would a - hunt - ing go, And

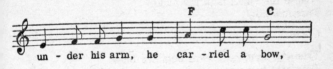

un - der his arm, he car - ried a bow,

All for to shoot a mer-ry lit-tle doe a-

mong the leaves so —— green, O.

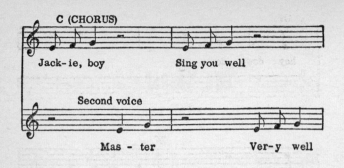

C (CHORUS)

Jack-ie, boy

Sing you well

Second voice

Mas - ter

Ver-y well

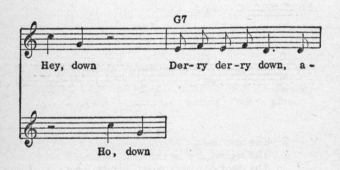

G7

Hey, down

Der-ry der-ry down, a-

Ho, down

C   G7   G7   C

mong the leaves so — green, O. To my

hey down, down

To my ho down, down

Hey, down

Der-ry, der-ry down, A-

Ho down

mong the leaves so green - O.

2. The first doe he shot at, he missed
   The second doe he trimmed, he kissed
   The third doe went where nobody wist
   Among the leaves so green, O.

   Chorus

3. The fourth doe she did cross the plain
   The Keeper fetched her back again
   Where it is now it must remain
   Among the leaves so green, O.

   Chorus

4. The fifth doe she did cross the brook
   The Keeper fetched it back with his crook
   Where it is now you must go and look
   Among the leaves so green, O.

   Chorus

The Leather-Winged Bat

Called also "The Birds Courting Song." The last verse is my own addition.

Em / Bm

"Hi", said the Lit-tle Leath-er Winged Bat

Em / G

"I'll tell you the rea-son that, the

Em

rea-son that I fly in the night, It's be-

Em / Bm / Em

cause I lost my heart's de light."

CHORUS

Em / Bm

How- de -dow- de did-dle -oh- day

How - de - dow- de   did - dle - oh - day.

How - de - dow - de   did - dle - oh - day.

Ful - lul - lee - de   did - dle - de - doh.

2. "Hi," said the woodpecker, sittin' on the fence,
   "Once I married a handsome wench
   She got saucy and from me fled
   Ever since then, my hair's been red."

Chorus

3. "Hi," said the bluebird, as she flew,
   "If I had my way, I'd have two
   If one got saucy and wanted to go
   I'd have two strings for my bow."

Chorus

4. "Hi," said the little birds circling around,
   "We fly in circles above the ground
   The circles get smaller every year
   And by and by, we disappear."

Chorus

Little Bitty Baby

Originally the song was sung by an *a cappella* rural Negro church choir. This tune is an approximation of a very subtle, primitive, contrapuntal choral setting, and I have changed some of the words to conform more logically to the numbers.

Chil-dren, go, I will send thee. How will I send thee? I'm a-gon-na send thee one by one. One's for the lit-tle bit-ty bab-y who's born, born, born in Beth-le-hem.

(As each number is reached, the music of the seventh and eighth bar above is simply repeated backwards through number one)

2. Children, go, I will send thee
   How will I send thee?
   I'm a-gonna send thee two by two
   Two's for Joseph and Mary
   One's for the little bitty Baby
   Who's born, born, born in Bethlehem.

3. Three's for the three old wise men . . .

4. Four's for the four who stood at the door . . .

5. Five's for the Hebrew Children . . .

6. Six for the six who had to get fixed . . .

7. Seven for the seven who went to Heaven . . .

Lord Randal

A folk song that has crept into the concert repertoire. The famous British collector-arranger, Cecil Sharpe, collected this song at least twenty times in England and here as many times.

Freely

Where have you been all the day
Ran-dal, my son? Where have you been all the day,
my pret-ty one? I've been to my sweet-heart
moth-er. I've been to my sweet-heart
Moth-er.___ Make my bed soon, For I'm
sick to my heart, and I fain would lie down.

What have you been eating, Randal, my son?
What have you been eating, my pretty one?
Oh, eels and eel broth, mother,
Oh, eels and eel broth, mother.
Make my bed soon, etc.

Where did she get them from, Randal, my son?
Where did she get them from, my pretty one?
From hedges and ditches, mother,
From hedges and ditches, mother.
Make my bed soon, etc.

What will you leave your father, Randal, my son?
What will you leave your father, my pretty one?
My land and my houses, mother,
My land and my houses, mother.
Make my bed soon, etc.

What will you leave your mother, Randal, my son?
What will you leave your mother, my pretty one?
My gold and my silver, mother,
My gold and my silver, mother.
Make my bed soon, etc.

What will you leave your sweetheart, Randal, my son?
What will you leave your sweetheart, my pretty one?
A rope to hang her, mother!
A rope to hang her, mother!
Make my bed soon, etc.

The Midnight Special

Trains have always played a major role in the folklore of America. They are still objects of romantic admiration, as witness the enormous toy train industry here.

Well, you wake up in the morn - ing hear the ding - song ring. You go a-march-in' to the ta - ble, it's the same damn thing. Well, it's on a one -a ta - ble knife and fork and a pan. And if you say a thing a-bout it, you're in trou-ble with the man.

CHORUS

Let the Mid-night Spec-ial shine its light on me.— Let the Mid-night Spec-ial shine its ev-er-lov-in' light on me.

2. If you go to Houston, you better walk right
   You better not stagger, you better not fight,
   Or Sheriff Benson will arrest you, he will carry you down,
   If the jury finds you guilty, you'll be penitentiary bound,

   Chorus

3. Yonder comes l'il Rosie. How in the world do you know?
   I can tell her by her apron, and the dress she wore,
   Umberella on her shoulder, piece of paper in her hand.
   Well, I heard her tell her captain: "I want my man."

   Chorus

4. I'm gwine away to leave you, and my time ain't long
   The man is gonna call me, and I'm goin' home
   Then I'll be done all my grievin', whoopin' hollerin' and
       a-cryin'
   Then I'll be done all my studyin' 'bout my great long time.

   Chorus

5. Well, the biscuit's on the table, just as hard as any rock
   If you try to swallow them, break a convict's heart.
   My sister wrote a letter, my mother wrote a card
   If you want to come and see us, you'll have to ride the
       rods.

   Chorus

Motherless Child

I believe that this one spiritual alone, if none other had ever been written, would move the world to love and admire the musical genius of the Negro.

Some-times I feel like a Moth-er-less child.

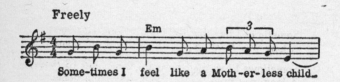

— Some - times I feel like a

moth - er - less child. Some - times I

feel like a moth - er - less child.

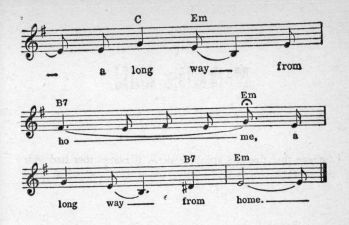

a long way ___ from ho ___ me, a long way ___ from home. ___

2. Sometimes I feel that the night is long (*3 times*)
   A long way from home; a long way from home.

3. Sometimes I feel that the night won't end (*3 times*)
   A long way from home; a long way from home.

Oh Freedom

For some unknown reason, this spiritual is not so well known as some of the others, although it ranks with the best. Sometimes a line is sung: "....I'll be buried in my grave, and take my place with those who loved and fought before..."

Oh, _____ free-dom, free-dom

Oh, _____ free-dom Oh,

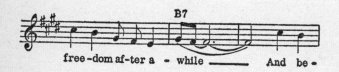

free-dom af-ter a - while _____ And be -

fore I'd be a sla - ve, I'll be

bur - ied in my grave, and go

home to— my Lord— and be free.—

2. No more mourning, mourning
    No more weeping
    No more misery after a while
    And before I'd be a slave
    I'll be buried in my grave
    And go home to my Lord and be free.

3. *Repeat first verse*

Old Smoky

Attained the number one spot on the nation's hit parade by virtue of a recording of the Weavers.

On top of Old Smok-

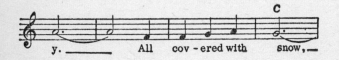

y. All cov-ered with snow,

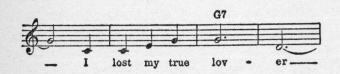

I lost my true lov-er

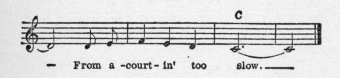

From a -court-in' too slow.

2. On top of Old Smoky, I went there to weep
   Cause a false-hearted lover, is worse than a thief.

3. For a thief he will rob you, and take what you have
   But a false-hearted lover, will send you to your grave.

4. She'll hug you and kiss you, and tell you more lies
   Than the cross-ties on a railroad, and stars in the skies.

5. Come all you fair maidens, take warning from me
   Don't place your affections in a green willow tree.

6. For the roots they will wither, and the leaves they will die
   And you'll soon be forgotten, and never know why.

7. On top of Old Smoky, all covered with snow
   I lost my true lover, from a-courtin' too slow.

Paper of Pins

A courtin' song, pure and simple, and shrewd. Its English counterpart is "The Keys of Canterbury," with a similar practical denouement.

Two-beat rhythm

I'll give to you a pa-per of pins, For that's the way my love be-gins, If you will mar-ry me, me, me, If you will mar-ry me._____

2. I'll not accept a paper of pins
   If that's the way your love begins
   And I won't marry you, you, you
   And I won't marry you.

3. I'll give to you a coach and four
   That you may ride from door to door, etc.

4. I'll give to you a little dog
   To take with you abroad, abroad, etc.

5. I'll give to you a dappled horse
   So's you can ride from cross to cross, etc.

6. I'll give to you a gown of green
   So's you can look like any queen, etc.

7. I'll give to you my hand and my heart
   So's we can marry and never part, etc.

8. I'll give to you the keys of my chest
   So's you can have gold at your request
   If you will marry me, me, me
   If you will marry me.

9. Oh yes, I'll take the keys of your chest
   So I can have gold at my request
   And I will marry you, you, you
   And I will marry you.

10. And now I see that money is all
    And your love is nothing at all
    So I won't marry you, you, you
    And I won't marry you.

11. Well, then, I'll be an old, old maid
    And take my chair and sit in the shade
    And I will marry none at all
    I'll marry none at all.

Pat Works on the Railway

Or, "Pat Works on the Erie." A song which goes back to the early days of the building of the American railroads, when Irish immigrants built them, in the East anyhow.

Two-beat rhythm

Am

1. In eigh - teen hun - dred and for - ty one, I
2. When we left Ire - land to come here to

C

put me cor - du - roy breech - es on, I
spend our lat - ter days in cheer, The

Am

put me cor - du - roy breech - es on to
boss he drank some gin - ger beer, While

Am   Dm   Am

work up - on the rail - way.
Pat worked on the rail - way.

CHORUS Am

Fil - le - me - oo - re - oo - re - ay

Fil - le - me - oo - re - oo - re - ay.

Fil - le - me - oo - re - oo - re - ay To

work up - on the rail - way.

3. It's "Pat do this" and "Pat do that" without a stocking or
   a cravat.
   And nothing but an old straw hat while working on the
   railway.

4. And when Pat lays him down to sleep the wiry bugs
   around him creep.
   Divil a bit can poor Pat sleep while working on the railway.

5. In eighteen hundred and forty-three twas then he met
   sweet Biddy McGee.
   An illy gatt wife she was to see while working on the
   railway.

6. In eighteen hundred and forty-seven sweet Biddy McGee
   she went to heaven
   If she had one child she had eleven to work upon the
   railway.

Peter Grey

This was once a serious song, but it metamorphosed into a parody of itself, the fate of many a purple piece of bravura.

Freely

Once on a time, there lived a man; His name was Pet - er Grey, ___ He lived way down in that there town, called Penn - syl - van - i - ay.

CHORUS

Blow ye winds of the morn - ing,

Blow ye winds hi - ho.

Blow ye winds of the morn-ing__ Blow, blow, blow!

2. Now Peter fell in love all with
   A nice young girl
   The first three letters of her name
   Were Lucy, Annie, Pearl

   Chorus

3. When Lucy's father heard of this
   He straightaway said, "No!"
   And quin-ci-cont-ly she was sent
   Beyond the O-hio.

   Chorus

4. Then Peter went away out West
   To seek his for-ti-an
   But he was caught and scal-pi-ed
   By a bloody In-di-an.

   Chorus

5. When Lucy heard of this sad news
   She knew not what to say
   She wep' and wep' and wep-i-ed
   Her pore sweet life a-way.

   Chorus

117

The Riddle Song

Apparently the earliest versions of this song were collected by Cecil Sharpe in the Southern Mountains before the First World War.

Freely

I gave my love a cher - ry, that

has no ____ stone, I

gave my love a chick - en that

has no ____ bone. I

told my love a stor - y that

has no ——— end, And I

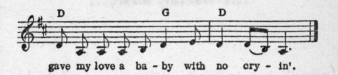

gave my love a ba - by with no cry - in'.

2. How can there be a cherry that has no stone?
   How can there be a chicken that has no bone?
   How can there be a story that has no end?
   How can there be a baby with no cryin'?

3. A cherry when in blossom, it has no stone
   A chicken that is pippin', it has no bone
   The story that I love you, it has no end
   And a baby that is sleepin', has no cryin'.

The Roving Gambler

American songs are full of "ramblers," "gamblers," strayers, wanderers, rovers, and the like. As Leadbelly's song "Irene" says: "Stop ramblin', stop gamblin', stop stayin' out late at night . . ."

I am a rov - ing

gam - bler, I gam - ble down— in

town. Where - ev - er I meet with a

deck of cards,—I lay my mon - ey down.

2. I had not been in Washington, many more weeks than three
   When I fell in love with a pretty little gal, and she fell in love with me.

3. She took me in her parlor; she cooled me with her fan
   She whispered soft in her mother's ear: "I love this gamblin' man."

4. "O daughter, O dear daughter, why do you treat me so?
   To leave your dear old mother, and with a gambler go."

5. "O mother, O dear mother, you know I love you well
   But the love I have for the gambling man no human tongue can tell."

6. I've gambled down in Washington, I've gambled down in Spain
   I'm going down to Georgia to gamble my last game.

7. I hear the train a-comin', a-comin' round the curve
   A-whistlin' and a-blowin', and a-strainin' every nerve.

8. "O mother, O dear mother, I'll tell you if I can
   If you ever see me comin' back it'll be with a gamblin' man."

Shenando'

One of the most requested songs. The reason lies mostly in the tune, for the lyric says nothing unusual to warrant the interest in this song, an interest which does not seem to diminish.

Freely

Oh Shen - an - do' I love your daugh- ter.__ Hi - Ho, You roll - in' riv - er__ Oh Shen-an -do', I love your daugh- ter. A - way, I'm bound a -way to the broad Mis - sou - ri.

2. For seven long years I courted Nancy.
   Hi, ho, you rolling river
   For seven long years I courted Nancy
   Away, I'm bound away
   To the rolling river.

3. She went away and took another
   Hi, ho, you rolling river
   She went away and took another
   Away, I'm bound away
   To the rolling river.

4. *Repeat first verse*

Skip to My Lou

Long after adults, with their jaded and faded tastes, tire of this song, the children keep singing it.

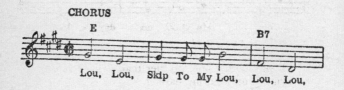

CHORUS

Lou, Lou, Skip To My Lou, Lou, Lou,

Skip To My Lou, Lou, Lou, Skip To My Lou,

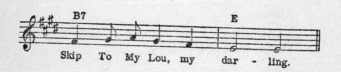

Skip To My Lou, my dar - ling.

VERSE

Lost my part - ner, What'll I do?

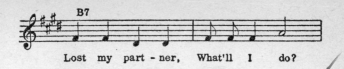

Lost my part - ner, What'll I do?

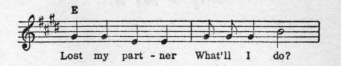

Lost my part - ner What'll I do?

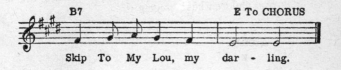

Skip To My Lou, my dar - ling.

2. I'll get another one, prettier than you (*3 times*)
   Skip to my Lou, my darling.

   Chorus

3. Gone again, skip to my Lou (*3 times*)
   Skip to my Lou, my darling.

   Chorus

4. Fly's in the buttermilk, shoo, shoo, shoo (*3 times*)
   Skip to my Lou, my darling.

   Chorus

5. A little red wagon, painted blue (*3 times*)
   Skip to my Lou, my darling.

   Chorus

Sourwood Mountain

A square-dance, breakdown, hoedown, fiddlin', jiggin', dancin', prancin' tune. Choose yore pardners.

Chick-ens a-crow-in' on Sour-wood Moun-tain

Ho — de —ing — dong — doo-dle -al -ley-day.

So man-y pret-ty gals, I can't count 'em.

Ho — de—ing — dong -doo-dle al -ley-day.

2. My true love's a blue-eyed daisy
   Ho-de-ing-dong- etc.
   If she won't marry me, I'll go crazy, etc.

3. My true love's a blue-eyed dandy, etc.
   She's as sweet as taffy candy, etc.

4. I got a gal at the head of the holler, etc.
   If she won't come, then I won't call 'er, etc.

The Sow Got the Measles

"... and she died in the spring ..."

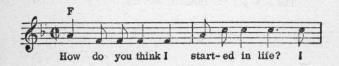

How do you think I start-ed in life? I

got me a sow and oth-er such things.

Pig or hog or an-y such thing, The

sow got the meas-les and she died in the spring.

2. What do you think I made of her hide?
   Made the best saddle you ever did ride.
   Saddle or bridle or any such thing,
   The sow got the measles and she died in the spring.

128

3. What do you think I did with her tail?
   Made me a whip and also a flail.
   Whip or whip-handle, any such thing,
   The sow got the measles and she died in the spring.

4. What do you think I made of her hair?
   Made the best satin you ever did wear.
   Satin or silk or any such thing,
   The sow got the measles and she died in the spring.

5. What do you think I did with her feet?
   Made the best pickles you ever did eat.
   Pickles or glue or some such thing,
   The sow got the measles and she died in the spring.

Spanish Is the Loving Tongue

My friend, Louis L'Amour, fine writer, fine fellow, tells me he heard this in the Southwest many years ago. I heard it in the Northeast not so many years ago.

Span-ish is the lov-ing tongue, Soft as

mus-ic, Light as spray,— 'Twas a girl I

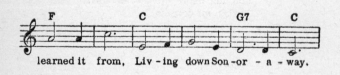

learned it from, Liv-ing down Son-or - a - way.

I don't look much like a lov-er, Yet I

say her loved words o-ver of-ten when I'm

all a lone: "Mi a-mor, mi cor-a-zon."

2. Moonlight on the patio
   Old señora nodding near
   Me and Juana talking low
   So her madre couldn't hear
   How the hours would go a-flying
   And too soon I'd hear her sighing
   In her little sorry tone,
   "Mi amor, mi corazon."

3. Never seen her since that night
   I can't cross the line, you know
   Wanted for a gambling fight
   Like as not it's better so
   Yet I've always sort of missed her
   Since that last sad night I kissed her
   Left her heart and lost my own,
   "Adios, mi corazon."

Springfield Mountain

Here is an example of a song about a specific, known incident. It seems that a young man named Timothy Myrick of Springfield Mountain, Massachusetts, (now Wilbraham), died of the bite of a rattlesnake in Farmington, Connecticut, on August 7, 1761. He was then engaged to a Miss Molly (or Sally) Curtis. The ballad, originally meant to be serious, survived the snakebite, otherwise fatal.

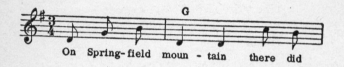

On Spring-field moun - tain there did

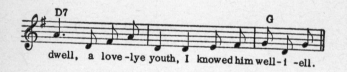

dwell, a love -lye youth, I knowed him well- i -ell.

CHORUS

Too - roo - de - nay, Too - roo - de

noo, Too-roo - de - nay, Too-roo - de - noo.

2. This love-lye youth, one day did go
   Down to the meadow for to mow-i-ow

   Chorus

3. He scarce had mowed twice round the field
   When a cru-el sarpint bit his heel-i-eel.

   Chorus

4. They took him home to Mollye dear
   Which made him feel so very queer-i-eer.

   Chorus

5. Now Molly had two rubye lips
   With which the pizen she did sip-iip.

   Chorus

6. Now Molly had a rotting tooth
   And so the pizen kilt them both-i-oth.

   Chorus

The Streets of Laredo

One of the most famous of all cowboy songs goes back to early English sources. Many towns besides Laredo claim the hero for their own, in other versions.

As I walked out in the Streets of La-red-o, As I walked out in La-re-do one day, I spied a poor cow-boy all wrapped in white lin-en, All wrapped in white lin-en, As cold as the clay.

2. "I see by your outfit that you are a cowboy,"
   These words he did say as I boldly walked by
   "Come set down beside me and hear my sad story
   I'm just a young cowboy and know I must die."

3. 'Twas once in the saddle, I used to go dashing
   'Twas once in the saddle I used to go gay
   First down to Rosie's and then to the cardhouse
   I'm shot in the breast and I'm dying today.

4. Get sixteen gamblers to carry my coffin
   Get six pretty maidens to sing me a song
   Take me to the graveyard and lay the sod o'er me
   I'm just a young cowboy and I know I done wrong.

5. Oh beat the drum slowly, and play the fife lowly
   Play the dead march as you carry me along
   Put bunches of roses all over my coffin
   Roses to deaden the clods as they fall.

6. *Repeat first verse*

Sweet Betsy from Pike

The ballad, par excellence, of the days of '49, when Sweet Betsy and Ike along with many fellow Americans, westered in the gold rush.

Oh, don't you re-mem-ber, Sweet Bet-sy from Pike, She crossed the big moun-tains with her lov-er Ike, With two yoke of ox-en and one yal-ler dog, And an old Shang Hai roost-er and one spot-ted hog.

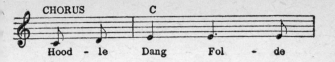

CHORUS

C

Hood - le   Dang   Fol - de

G7   C

di - do Hood-le Dang Fol - de - day.

2. They got to the desert where Betsy give out
   Down on the sand she lay rolling about
   Ike he gazed at her with sobs and with sighs
   Won't you get up sweet Betsy, you'll get sand in your
       eyes.

   Chorus

3. Well, the oxen run off and the Shanghai it died
   The last piece of bacon that morning was fried
   Ike got discouraged and Betsy got mad
   And the dog wagged his tail and looked wonderfully sad.

   Chorus

4. Ike and sweet Betsy attended a dance
   Ike wore a pair of his Pike County pants
   Betsy was dressed up in ribbons and rings
   Quoth Ike, "You're an angel, but where are your wings?"

   Chorus

5. A miner come up, says, "Will you dance with me?"
   "I will, you old hoss, if you don't make too free,
   Tell you the reason, if you want to know why,
   Doggone you I'm chock full of strong alkali."

   Chorus

Tam Pierce

(Widdicombe Fair)

When I first heard "Tam Pierce," something made me wonder why the horse and the men were turned into ghosts. It developed that I had heard a shortened version of a longer ballad, which explains all. The key words are ". . . and see his old mare a-makin' her will . . ."

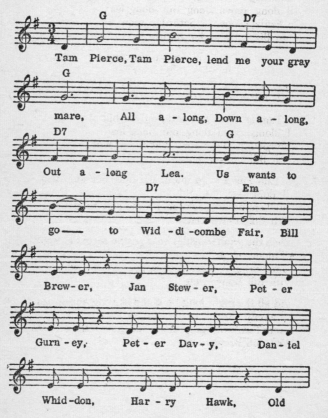

Tam Pierce, Tam Pierce, lend me your gray mare, All a-long, Down a-long, Out a-long Lea. Us wants to go to Wid-di-combe Fair, Bill Brew-er, Jan Stew-er, Pet-er Gurn-ey, Pet-er Dav-y, Dan-iel Whid-don, Har-ry Hawk, Old

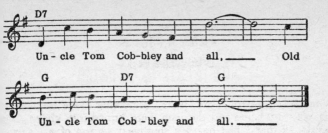

Un - cle Tom Cob-bley and all,____ Old

Un - cle Tom Cob - bley and all.____

2. When shall I see again my gray mare?
   All along, down along, out along lea
   By Friday noon, or Saturday soon
   With Bill Brewer, Jan Stewer, etc.

3. Then Friday came and Saturday soon
   All along, down along, out along lea
   And Tam's old mare she ne'er did come home
   With Bill Brewer, etc.

4. So Tam he went to the top of the hill
   All along, down along, out along lea
   And seed his old mare a-makin' her will
   With Bill Brewer, etc.

5. So Tam Pierce's old mare, she took sick and died
   All along, etc.
   And Tam he sat down on a stone and cried
   With Bill Brewer, etc.

6. When the wind whistles cold on the moors at night
   All along, etc.
   Tam's old gray mare doth appear ghastly white
   With Bill Brewer, etc.

7. And all the night long be heard skirling and groans
   All along, etc.
   From Tam's old gray mare and her rattling bones
   With Bill Brewer, etc.

The Trail to Mexico

Who was A. J. Stinson? No one knows now, but his name lives on in this "cow-trail classic."

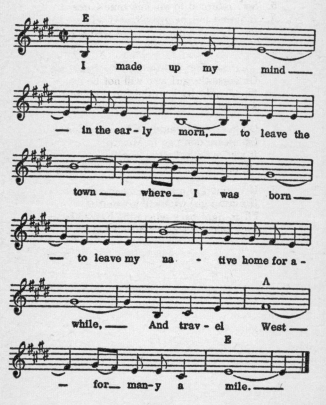

I made up my mind — in the ear-ly morn, — to leave the town — where I was born — — to leave my na - tive home for a - while, — And trav-el West — — for — man-y a mile. —

140

2. 'Twas in the year of eighty-three
   That A. J. Stinson he hired me
   He said, "Young man, I want you to go,
   And follow my herd to Mexico."

3. 'Twas in the springtime of the year
   I volunteered to drive the steers
   I'll tell you boys, 'twas a long hard go
   As the trail rolled on into Mexico.

4. When I arrived in Mexico
   I wanted my girl, but I could not go
   So I wrote a letter to my dear,
   But not a word from her did I hear.

5. So I returned to my one time home
   Inquired for the girl whom I adore
   She said, "Young man, I've wed a richer life,
   Therefore, young fellow, get another wife."

6. Oh curse your gold and your silver, too
   Oh curse the girl who will not be true
   I'll go right back to the Rio Grande
   And get me a job with a cowboy band.

7. Oh buddy, Oh buddy, Oh please don't go
   Oh please don't go to Mexico
   If you've no girl more true than I
   Oh please don't go where the bullets fly.

8. If I've no girl more true than you
   If I've no girl who will prove true
   I'll go right back where the bullets fly
   And follow the cow-trail till I die.

The Twelve Days of Christmas

Almost every Western country has its "cumulative" song or songs. When I made the first recorded version of "The Twelve Days of Christmas," on an old 78 r.p.m. shellac record, I didn't have have room enough on one side to sing every verse in its entirety.

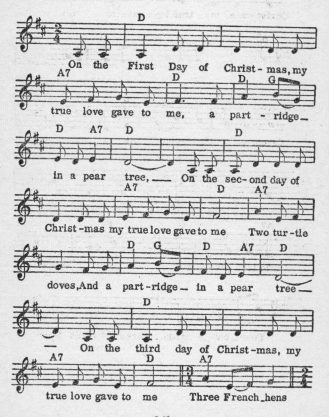

Two tur-tle doves, And a part-ridge— in a pear tree. —— On the fourth day of Christ-mas, my true love gave to me Four col-ly birds, three French hens, two tur-tle doves, and a part-ridge— in a pear tree— —— On the fifth day of Christ-mas, my true love gave to me Five gold— rings. Four— col-ly birds, three French hens

(Each succeeding verse, or number, has the same tune as number 6, after which the song proceeds from 5 down to the end as above.)

7 swans a-swimming . . .

8 maids a-milking

9 pipers piping

10 ladies dancing

11 Lords a-leaping

12 fiddlers fiddling

Uncle Reuben

I learned this charming Southern song from Ruth Cleveland in New York City in 1938. It was a lucky find, for it had never previously appeared in print or on records.

CHORUS   C

Un - cle Reu - ben caught a coon, done

(Whispered)   (Whispered)

gone, Chick - a - chick, Done gone, Chick - a - chick, Done

(Whispered)

gone, Chick-a-chick, Un-cle Reu-ben caught a coon, done

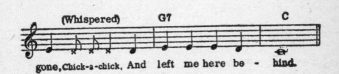

(Whispered)   G7   C

gone, Chick-a-chick, And left me here be - hind.

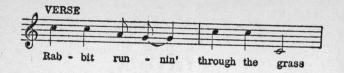

VERSE

Rab - bit run - nin' through the grass

G7   C

Fox - es close be - hind. Trees and weeds and

To CHORUS

G7   C

cock - le - burrs is all the fox - es find.

2. Possum up a 'simmon tree
   Raccoon on the ground
   Raccoon say, "Mr. Possum, won't you shake one 'simmon
     down."

   Chorus

3. If you love me, Liza Jane
   Put your hand in mine
   You won't lack for no corn-bread
   As long as the sun do shine.

   Chorus

146

Venezuela

John Jacob Niles, who has made some brilliantly permanent contributions to folk song, found this song in Liverpool around the time of World War I.

I met her in Ven-e-zu - e - e -

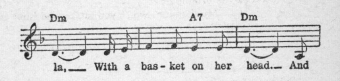

la,__ With a bas-ket on her head.__ And

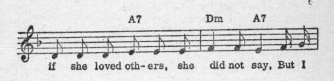

if she loved oth-ers, she did not say, But I

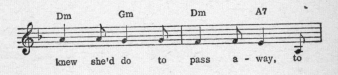

knew she'd do to pass a - way, to

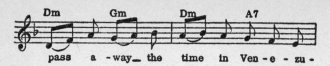

pass a -way— the time in Ven-e-zu-

-e - la, To pass— a - way— the

time in Ven-e-zu - e • e - la. —

2. I gave her a silken sash of blue, a silken sash of blue
   Because I knew that she would do
   With all of the tricks I knew she knew
   To pass away the time in Venezuela,
   To pass away the time in Venezuela.

3. And when the wind was out to sea, the wind was out to
      sea
   And she was a-taking leave of me
   I said, "Cheer up, there'll always be
   Sailors ashore with leave in Venezuela,
   Sailors ashore with leave in Venezuela."

4. Her lingo was strange but the thought of her smile
   The thought of her wonderful smile
   Will haunt me and taunt me for many a mile
   For she was my gal and she helped the while
   To pass away the time in Venezuela,
   To pass away the time in Venezuela.

Wayfaring Stranger

What is known technically as a "white spiritual," a term I feel we can do without.

Freely

I'm just a poor, — Way-far-ing

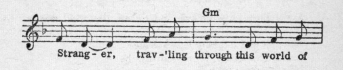

Strang-er, trav-'ling through this world of

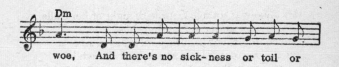

woe, And there's no sick-ness or toil or

trou-ble — in that fair land to which I

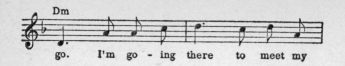

go. I'm go - ing there to meet my

moth-er, I'm go - ing there no more to

- roam, I'm just a - go - ing o - ver

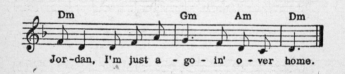

Jor-dan, I'm just a - go - in' o - ver home.

2. I'm just a poor wayfaring stranger
   Traveling through this world of woe
   And there's no sickness, or toil or trouble
   In that fair land to which I go
   I'm going there to meet my father
   I'm going there no more to roam
   I'm just a-goin' over Jordan
   I'm just a-goin' over home.

A Worried Man

by Tom Glazer and Dave Guard

Here is a new version of this famous old folk song, which the Kingston Trio recorded and made into a hit-parade song in 1959.

CHORUS

It takes a wor-ried man to sing a wor-ried song It takes a wor-ried man to sing a wor-ried song It takes a wor-ried man to sing a wor-ried song, I'm wor-ried now ___ but I won't be wor-ried long ___

VERSE

Got my-self a Cad-il-lac ___

151

thirt-y dol-lars down ___ Got my-self a

brand new house___ five miles out of town

Got my-self a gal named Sue___ treats me real-ly

fine, She is my ba - by _____ and I

love her all the time _____ (It)

2. I've been away on a business trip
   Travelin' all around
   I've got a gal and her name is Sue
   Prettiest gal in town
   She sets my mind to worryin'
   Every time I'm gone
   I'll be home tonight
   So I won't be worried long.
   Chorus

3. Well, Bobby's in the living room
   Holding hands with Sue
   Nicki's at that big front door
   About to come on through
   I'm here in the closet
   Oh Lord, what shall I do
   We're worried now, but we won't be worried long.
   Chorus

Yankee Doodle

Most of us remember only one stanza of this fine song: "... stuck a feather in his hat and called it macaroni ..." but there are other good ones. I particularly like the rhyme of the name Captain Goodin' with hasty puddin'.

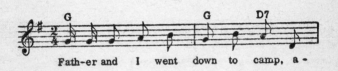

Fath-er and I went down to camp, a-

long with Cap - tain Good - in, And

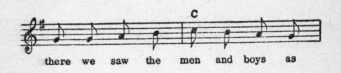

there we saw the men and boys as

thick as hast - y pud - din'.

C (CHORUS)

Yank - ee Doo - dle keep it up,

G

Yank - ee Doo - dle dand y.

C

Mind the mus - ic and the step and

G D7 G

with the girls be hand - y.

2. And there was Captain Washington
   Upon a slapping stallion
   And all the men and boys around
   I guess there was a million.

   Chorus

3. Yankee Doodle went to town
   Riding on a pony
   Stuck a feather in his hat
   And called it macaroni.

   Chorus

Ballad singers of yore often wrote songs, and often wrote good ones. To prove that this tradition has not died, here are three examples by three contemporary ballad singers: "So We'll Go No More A-Roving," Richard Dyer-Bennet's setting to the Byron poem; "Tibbie Dunbar," Burl Ives' setting to a poem of Robert Burns; and "With Rue My Heart Is Laden," the poem by A. E. Housman, with my music.

Why include these in a collection of folk songs? Aren't they composed songs, art songs, if you will—the exact antithesis of anybody's definition of a folk song?

Well, anybody's definition is not necessarily ours. We feel quite strongly that there is a great similarity in feeling if not in form between these songs and folk songs. We feel that a clue to this feeling is the obvious fact that three folk singers (or singers of folk songs, if you want to be strict about it) wrote the tunes.

There are many, many examples of songs called folk songs which express poetry as pure and intense, as immediate and moving, as any lyric by a known poet, although not often as complex. I have often found it necessary, in singing these three songs, to speak the lyric first, and then sing the song, because as a rule a poem, worked over and over, (consciously or unconsciously) molded, condensed, wrought—takes more than one reading. But so do some folk song lyrics.

In any case, the important thing is the song. These are lovely, simple settings to simple, lovely lyrics. We suspect the poets would have enjoyed hearing their poems sung to these tunes.

As a final thought: it occurred to me, in discussing whether or not to include these songs, that a song by Purcell, say, could easily have been lost many years ago, and could then have reappeared as a folk song, sung with appropriate regional flourishes and grammatical lapses, at which point it could have finally been collected by the usual enthusiastic collector, and have appeared in an appropriate folk song collection. Is there no line, then, between a folk song and one written by a known writer? There is, but it is not so fine, in our opinion, as is usually thought. It is a line like a river, sometimes narrow, sometimes broad; sometimes straight, sometimes crooked; even underground sometimes. Therefore, these songs are here.

T.G.

So We'll Go No More A-Roving

Poem by Byron   Tune by Richard Dyer-Bennet

Note: No chord-symbols were put here out of respect for Mr. Dyer-Bennet's guitar accompaniment, which is something more than simple strumming.

So we'll go no more a - rov -

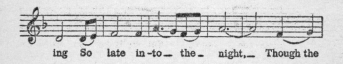

ing So late in -to the night,— Though the

heart be still as lov - ing, and the moon be

still as bright. For the sword out - wears its

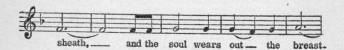

sheath,—— and the soul wears out the breast.

And the heart must pause‿ to breathe,— And love it‿self‿must rest.‿ Though the night was

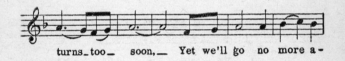

made‿ for lov‿ing, And the day re‿

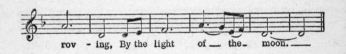

turns‿too‿ soon,— Yet we'll go no more a‿

rov‿ing, By the light of‿ the‿ moon.‿

Tibbie Dunbar

Poem by Robert Burns   Tune by Burl Ives

Wilt thou come with me, sweet
Tib-bie Dun-bar? Wilt thou come with me, sweet
Tib - bie Dun - bar? Wilt thou
ride on a horse, or be drawn in a car,— Or
walk by my side, O sweet Tib-bie Dun-bar? I

158

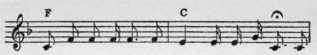

care not thy dad-dy, his land and his mon-ey; I

care not thy kin   sae high and sae laird-ly; But

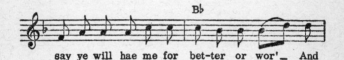

say ye will hae me for bet-ter or wor'_ And

come in thy coat-ie, sweet Tib-bie Dun-bar,

Say ye will hae me for bet-ter or wor'_ And

come in   thy coat-tie, sweet Tib-bie Dun-bar.

With Rue My Heart Is Laden

Poem by A. E. Housman   Music by Tom Glazer

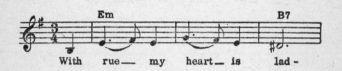

With rue— my heart— is lad-

en, For gold - en friends— I had.—

— For man - y a rose - lipt maid-

en, And man-y a light - foot lad. ___

___ By brooks_too broad_ for leap -

ing. The light - foot boys_ are laid. ___

___ The rose - lipt girls_ are sleep -

ing, In fields_where ros - es fade. ___

The Beginner Folk-Guitarist

The following is not meant to take the place of a teacher, because a good teacher is irreplaceable. However, most guitar instruction is not specifically intended for the amateur, who wants a minimum amount of technical burdens along with simple and musical results. This is an attempt in that direction.

Why Guitar? Why not banjo, or zither, or dulcimer, or uke, or piano? Because the guitar is the most popular instrument in use today for folk song accompaniment, and deservedly so, because it sounds good, is fairly easy on which to learn simple accompaniments quickly, and can accompany a wide range of different kinds of songs.

Kinds of Guitars. *The "f"-hole, or Jazz Guitar,* is not ordinarily used as a folk instrument because its tone is too big and brassy and not as mellow-sounding as the "folk" type. It gets its name from the two "f"-shaped holes like those of a violin. It can be played electrically or not, pick or plectrum

style, not with the fingers. The pick or plectrum referred to is a small, plastic, almost triangular shaped object which "picks" the strings to produce a sound as it is held between the thumb and forefinger of the right hand.

The *Electric Guitar* is used for special musical effects on popular records, and in Country-and-Western bands. It is not associated with individual folk accompaniment as a rule. The "f"-hole guitar can also be played electrically.

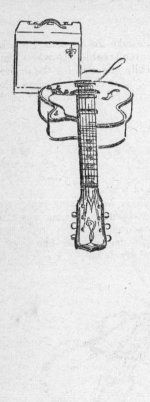

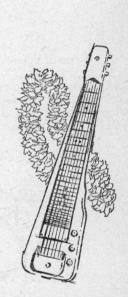

The *Hawaiian Guitar* looks different, and is tuned differently from other guitars. It not only is used in Hawaiian bands but also quite often in Country-and-Western bands. It is used mainly with other instruments. A very interesting, but rather rare, American folk-guitar style sounding like a Hawaiian guitar, is heard occasionally on old records, usually adapted to the blues.

The *Spanish Guitar* is also known as the Round-Hole Guitar, or the Flat-Top Guitar. *This is the guitar that will concern us.* It is tuned the same way as the "f"-hole guitar. The strings can be made of metals of various kinds or of gut or nylon. A true Spanish Guitar has strings only of gut or nylon, plus very soft metal strings usually wrapped around silk in the lower, or bass, strings

Other Guitars. Sometimes unusual guitars are seen, such as seven-string Russian guitars, or guitars with two necks, one of which contains extra bass strings, or guitars made of metal instead of wood, or 12-string round-hole guitars, but these are unorthodox. A beginner should learn first the Spanish or Spanish-type Guitar for best results.

Strings. Which kind to use, metal or nylon (gut)? Either can be used. Nylon-strung guitars are so called even though the bass strings are of soft metal. The difference? Nylon is somewhat easier on the fingers for a beginner, especially a woman, or lady, as they are called sometimes. But the mellow tone of nylon or gut is harder to produce. Metal strings can sound mellow, too, on a good guitar, and are more characteristic of traditional American folk song accompaniment. But gut or nylon is becoming more popular.

When to Start Learning. Any age at all if you dare, but you will probably be disappointed in any results before the age of ten or so, unless there is a skillful teacher. It depends on the size of the hands to some degree. Before this age, eager children might do better to wrestle with the more manageable ukulele. However, there is no age too young to learn, especially some musical theory and sight-singing. This I cannot overemphasize; it is easy and can be picked up anywhere, even in school.

Buying a Guitar. The better the instrument, the better the tone, and the easier to produce a good tone, but the more expensive it will be. As instruments go, though, guitars are relatively inexpensive, ranging in price from around fifty dollars to three or four hundred dollars, with the case extra. (Cases range from about fifteen dollars to forty dollars or more.)

A beginner should get the best guitar he can afford. If he is not sure how long he will stay interested he can buy a cheaper one first and a better one later. Try not to buy one by yourself; get someone who knows to help you, at least as far as telling you the various makes and prices and their relative merits and demerits.

What about secondhand guitars in or out of pawnshops or hockshops? Let the buyer beware, although it is not impossible to find a good buy. But here, too, someone should go along and help you. When guitars are popular as they are today, good buys in pawnshops are scarce. If you would like to wait for the next Depression you might find good buys in secondhand guitars then, but I hope you don't.

PLAYING THE GUITAR

First, a warning. Since people differ greatly in their natural musical ability, the following may or may not be enough to learn something all by yourself. But most of you will, and it will be as simple as I believe humanly possible.

Tuning the Guitar. This means, if you don't know it, arranging the six guitar strings to play their six proper notes. A guitar is tuned: E-A-D-G-B-E, from low string to high. Memorize this if you can. An easy way to remember the names of the strings in this order is to remember this corny sentence which I made up once: Every American Daughter Gets Babies Eagerly. (Or make up your own sentence.)

The ability to tune a guitar properly differs according to how good your musical "ear" is. Remember, though, that an "ear" can be trained, so don't get discouraged if tuning does not come easy at first.

A guitar string is tuned by turning the tuning pegs, called *tuning machines*, at the top of the guitar. Turning one way tunes the strings higher; turning the opposite way tunes the strings lower in pitch. Try this to get the feel of the tuning machines.

You find the proper note for each string in several ways:

(1) By using a guitar pitch-pipe, sold in most music stores.

(2) By using a piano to find the proper notes; or, by having someone else play the notes on the piano or other instrument.

(3) By using your own ear if you have perfect pitch, which means the ability to hear any note in your own head without reference first to an instrument or any outside tone. This is relatively rare.

(4) If all these methods fail, ask someone to help you until you learn to do it yourself. And you can, no matter how hopeless it seems at first.

The trickiest thing about tuning a guitar is the fact that strings can produce sounds in between the correct ones; the strings can get too low (flat) or too high (sharp) with the guitar just lying around, or because of the weather or other reasons. Therefore, you may have to listen hard to make sure the string is sounding correctly.

After a guitar is in relatively accurate tune, there is a way to get a more perfect accuracy. Find the note of the top string (high E, first string) on the second string, B. You will find this note on the fifth fret of the B string. Pressing the fifth fret, play the note E on the B string and match its tone against the E of the open first string. If they are exact, leave them alone. If the E on the B string is flat or sharp, change the B string accordingly by using the tuning machine. Then find the note B on the third or G string, and match the second and third strings. Then find the note C on the fourth or A string and match the third and fourth strings. Then do the same thing with the rest of the strings. If this is confusing, let it alone for the time being, and look at this again later; if still confusing, ask someone to explain.

Holding the Guitar. Beginners should play seated. A straight-backed chair with no arms is best. Place the back of the instrument against your stomach, with the underside of the guitar resting upon your upper left thigh where it joins your torso. Spread your legs slightly to permit the guitar to rest comfortably in this position. The guitar should slant slightly upward from your thigh to the left.

Your *right* hand now will fall naturally on the strings over the hole, while your *left* hand holds the guitar neck, in position to form *chords* by pressing the proper fingers on the proper strings, as will be shown.

The Right Hand. The *right hand* produces sounds by plucking or strumming the strings. We will number the fingers of both hands, thus: forefinger, one; middle finger, two; then, three and four, in order. The thumb will not be numbered.

The guitar strings will also be numbered. The lowest string in pitch and the thickest in thickness is number 6, then on up in pitch and downward in number to string number one, which is the highest in pitch and the thinnest in thinness.

Place your right hand on the strings, so that fingers one, two, and three fall on strings three, two, and one. This may sound confusing until you try it; you will find that these fingers naturally find these strings. Your thumb will now fall as naturally upon the lower three strings at will, numbers six, five, or four.

Pluck the top three strings (three, two, one) your three fingers are upon. This will produce a sound. Repeat this several times, getting used to it. Don't be afraid to pluck firmly. Pluck them simultaneously, then one by one. Plucking is done with the tips of your fingers, if you have no protruding nails, or, with your nails preferably, if they are not too long and pointed. Females, or ladies, will have to pare their nails. Ragged edges on nails will not do.

Next: pluck the three lower strings, one by one, with your thumb, which you will find moves mostly sideways in plucking. The same thing goes about tip of thumb and thumbnail as in the fingers; it is best to have a medium-sized thumbnail do the plucking, but a thumb tip will do.

Combining the Thumb and Fingers of Right Hand. When you combine the thumb and fingers of the right hand, you are ready to learn to *accompany* with the right hand, which means to pluck the strings in various ways to produce sounds that are suitable. The word *accompany* is used because what you will play will not be the *melody*, but a background, or *accompaniment* to the melody in the form of chords.

Before we combine the thumb and fingers of the right hand, however, we must say something about accompaniment itself. Accompaniment to simple songs can be simplified into three main kinds: *two-beat*, *three-beat*, and *free-style*. This means that the basic rhythm underlying simple songs is one of these three rhythms, two-beat, three-beat, or free-style. Typical two-beat songs are "Red River Valley," "Cindy," "Go Tell Aunt Rhody," and John Philip Sousa's "The Stars and Stripes Forever"—any march, any fox trot. Typical three-beat songs are any waltzes like "Down in the Valley" and "Old Smoky." If you still don't understand this, forget it, for you will learn to play these rhythms by rote. *Free-style rhythm* (my term) has no particularly obvious rhythm, and is accompanied in a freer, less rhythmic way. This, too, may be hard for you to understand from written words alone, but forget it for the time being. As a point of reference, the song "Black Is the Color of My True Love's Hair" is usually accompanied in free-style, where an occasional chord is strummed freely, instead of in a regular, repeated pattern.

Sometimes a song can be accompanied either rhythmically or in free-style, or part of either. For example, "The Foggy

Dew" is usually accompanied in free-style in the verse, and in a slow two-beat rhythm in the chorus.

If you listen to folk song records you will soon be able to differentiate between and among the various rhythms used in accompaniment.

Now, with this in mind, we are ready to combine the thumb and fingers of the right hand to produce these three basic accompaniments.

The Two-Beat Accompaniment. The thumb plucks one of the three lower (bass) strings first. Then the three fingers (1, 2, 3) simultaneously pluck strings 3, 2, 1. First the thumb, then the three fingers together. The thumb, then, is beat number *one*; the fingers beat number *two*. This is repeated alternately, thumb, fingers; thumb, fingers; one, two; one, two.

Which bass string does the thumb strike? At first, strike any one of the three; get used to striking all three at different times. The *proper* bass string to strike depends on the *chord*, which is producted by the *left* hand. This we will take up further on; for the moment, strike any one of the bass strings.

Practice this two-beat strum.

The Three-Beat Accompaniment. Here, the thumb again plucks or strums the first beat; but the fingers pluck the next *two* beats, so you get a rhythmic pattern of: thumb, fingers, fingers; thumb, fingers, fingers, and so on; or, one, two, three; one, two, three, and so on.

Practice this three-beat strum, again using any bass string.

The Free-Style Accompaniment. This is done easiest by running the thumb over the strings lightly but firmly from low to high, from bass to treble (high) strings. This is the simplest way; there are other ways.

The Left Hand. The left hand produces combinations of notes by pressing the strings against the neck of the guitar in various ways. These combinations also include notes of open, unpressed, strings, of course. These notes will not be heard until the right hand plucks the strings. (An exception which does not concern us occurs mostly in Spanish-Flamenco music, where occasionally the left hand plucks the strings of the neck to produce notes.)

The neck of the guitar is divided into segments called *frets*, separated by fret bars (see drawing). Each fret contains a single note on any single string.

In our simple method, the left and right hands playing in combination will produce *chords*. A chord in music, is a combination of three or more notes heard together which sound pleasing or related.

In playing with the left hand, *make sure*:

(1) That the left arm is well away from your body. The tendency of beginners is to keep their left arm too close; consciously move it out from your left side.

(2) That the hand curves around and over the guitar neck, so that your fingers form a decided arch as they press down on the strings. The palm of your left hand should be well above the neck of the instrument, and arching away from the neck.

(3) That the tips of the fingers be free of long nails; the fingertips press, not the nails.

(4) That the fingertips press only the proper string, so that the sides of the fingers do not touch adjacent strings. This happens to beginners quite often; watch out for it, for if a wrong string is touched even lightly, the tone of that string will be dampened or even silenced completely.

(5) That the strings be pressed down *firmly*. Do not get

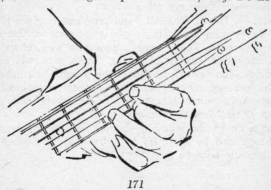

unhappy if your fingertips ache at first; you will get used to it as the fingertips harden gradually.

Chords. Here are diagrams of the commonest and simplest chords. They are often called "open string" chords, because they use a maximum of open strings and a minimum, therefore, of pressed-down strings (with the left hand); therefore, these are the easiest to play.

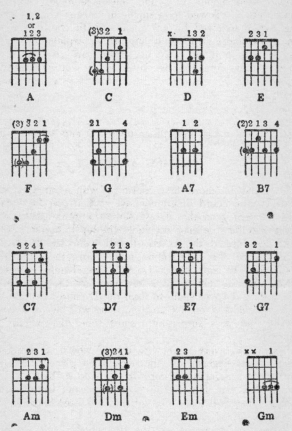

Explanation of Guitar Chord Diagrams:

The *numbers* over the diagrams refer to the fingers. The *dots* show where the fingers press the strings. Note that the

172

dots are not upon the fret-bars but just above them, yet not too far above them.

The "x" on any string means that the string is not played at all when these chords are played. Mainly this "x" will be found in the D and Dm chords.

The numbers and dots in parentheses indicate that these strings can be played alternately with the same finger.

The letters alone: A, C, etc., means a *major* chord; the capital letters followed by a small "m" means a minor chord. The capital followed by a 7 means a 7th chord. You may simply memorize all this without further explanation, or you may care to find out why the chords are so named, and wherein they differ. If the latter is so, you will need to consult a person who knows, or a suitable book on musical theory.

And now we will take two of the simplest chords above, learn to strum them suitably and apply them to accompanying an actual song. We will start with D and A7.

PLAYING A SONG

Take the D chord first. Form it with your left hand, following the chord diagram above. When you look at the diagram, remember that it represents the guitar neck as you *face* the guitar; the diagram shows the top four frets.

Having formed the D chord with your left hand, now strum it with your right thumb, going across the strings from low (thick) to high (thin). Do this several times.

Now practice taking your left hand off the guitar neck, and putting it down again to form the D chord. Do this over and over, off and on, off and on. This will be very tedious at first, but in a surprisingly short time, the tedium will diminish.

Now do the very same with the A7 chord. Form it, and remove your fingers from the neck, then place back again, and repeat several times until you can do it. Don't get discouraged if your fingers feel as if they can't learn to do it at first. They will learn. Be patient, and keep repeating the process.

When you have formed the two chords and strummed them both, you must now learn to change from one chord to the other and back again. This process will also be tedious at first, but keep at it. You will see, in changing from one chord to the next and back, that the best way is to make the change with minimum effort and maximum swiftness. In other words, when you remove your fingers from the neck to place them into position for the next chord, don't lift them off the neck too far.

Also: when forming any chord, resist the natural tendency to form the chord one finger at a time. Try very hard to practice forming the chord with your fingers moving *simultaneously*. This is not easy at first, but keep at it until it becomes second nature, for that is the way chords are finally formed when you master them.

Do all this very, very slowly at first, then gradually get faster.

After learning the D and A7 chords, which means learning to form them by heart, and to change from one to the other, strumming them, it is time to apply the two-beat and the three-beat accompaniments to them. This you have already started to do above. You will remember we postponed the problem of which of the three bass strings the thumb is to strike.

THE BASS STRINGS

Without going into musical theory, the beginner had best learn which bass string to strike in any given chord, by rote.

In a *two-beat strum*, when playing the D chord, your thumb first strikes the D bass string, followed by plucking the three upper strings of the chord. Then your thumb strikes the A bass string followed by the same plucking of the upper three strings of the chord. This alternating of the bass strings makes for a more interesting bass pattern than just repeating the D string in the bass over and over again monotonously.

When you play the D chord in a *three-beat strum*, the same thing happens except there are two plucks of the upper strings. In other words: beat one is the D string by the thumb; beats two and three are plucks of the upper three strings of the chord; the next beat one is the A string followed by the same plucks. Then back to D in the bass and then A as long as you are on the chord of D.

When you play the A7 chord, play the same bass strings alternately as in the D chord. You will find that the first note on the D string will be a different note (E) because your finger is pressing a different note when you play the A7 chord. But the second note in the bass of A7 will be the same (A) as in the D chord.

Now play the two chords in two-beat and three-beat rhythms, playing the proper bass strings.

When you can do this you are ready to apply these two chords to a real song.

PLAYING "DOWN IN THE VALLEY"

We are to learn to accompany the song "Down in the Valley," using the D and the A7 chords. This means we will be playing in the *key* of D. (If we played the song in other keys we would use other chord combinations.)

The first thing we have to know is, *When* do we play *which* of the two chords, for two is all we need? This we usually get from a printed copy of the song with the chords written over the melody. When one chord appears, it is played until the second chord appears, and so on. This song is printed in this book with the chords indicated. Refer to it.

The next thing we must do is to make sure we sing the song in the proper key, D. Many people can do this by "ear," that is, after hearing the first chord. If you can't, or are not sure, then you should know that the first note of the song is A. Strike A on the guitar, and that is the first note of the song to be sung.

Then, we must determine if the song is to be played in a two-beat, a three-beat, or a free-style rhythm. "Down in the Valley" is a three-beat song, basically, as you can see from the time-signature at the front of the song: ¾, which means that the numerator shows three beats to every measure, and the denominator shows that a quarter-note (4) is the symbol of one beat. (One beat can be symbolized by a whole note, 1, a half-note, 2, an eighth note, 8, a sixteenth note, 16, etc. The most common today are 4 and 8.)

Also, it may be superfluous to say so, but to accompany a song on the guitar, the melody must be known by heart, and the words too, preferably.

Now, we proceed with all that in mind. In order to see what happens exactly we have devised the following symbols: /, for a thumb stroke; U for the plucking by the three fingers. Here, then, is the first verse of "Down in the Valley," with the thumb and finger strokes indicated exactly as they occur:

D
/   u   u   /uu /uu/u   u
DOWN IN THE VAL-LEY, THE

A7
/   u   u /uu/uu
VAL-LEY SO LOW

/   u   u   /uu /uu/uu
HANG YOUR HEAD OV-ER

D
/   u   u   /uu/uu
HEAR THE WIND BLOW

Remember that each symbol (/ or U) represents one beat, either a thumb beat or a finger-pluck beat, and that each beat takes the same amount of time.

Note in the above verse that some words or syllables contain more than one beat, e.g., in the first line, VAL of VALLEY, contains three beats; while LEY of VALLEY contains five beats, and so forth.

Note also that you start on the D chord, and stay on it until you get to the word "LOW," where you change to the A7 chord, which you play until the last word "BLOW," where you change back to the D chord. And every verse follows the same pattern.

PLAYING A TWO-BEAT SONG

First, let us learn a new chord, G. (See chord diagrams.)
Then, having learned the G chord, practice changing from G to A7 and to D, and back again until you can change fairly well.

Now let us look at the song "Red River Valley." Here is one verse with our thumb-finger symbols indicated.

```
                 D
/     u    /u  /  u   /u  /   u   /    u  /u/u
(COME AND) SIT BY MY SIDE IF YOU LOVE ME


                              A7
/    u   /u   /   u   /u  /   u  /u/u/u
DO NOT HAST-EN TO BID ME A-DIEU


             D                                G
/    u   /u  /    u    /u   /   u   /   u  /u/u
BUT RE-MEM-BER THE RED RIV-ER VAL-LEY


         A7                                  D
/    u   /u  /    u    /u    /   u  /u/u/u
AND THE COWBOY WHO LOVED YOU SO TRUE
```

Note again that some words or syllables have more than one beat. Some have one beat, some two, and others more.

Note where the chords change.

Don't forget to alternate the bass strings.

The first two words are in parentheses because they can be started without guitar. These two beats are known as "pick-up" beats; a "pick-up" in a song is introductory in nature, and is often effective in a folk song when it starts with voice alone; in such a case, the guitar would start just after the "pick-up." If this is not clear, just start as indicated.

Again, make sure you know the melody before you start the guitar work, and make sure your starting note is accurate. Here, a second time, the first note is A, in this key, D, which note most people can get by ear if the first chord is strummed before the song proper starts.

All other verses follow similarly to the above verse.

PLAYING A SONG IN FREE-STYLE

Here, as mentioned earlier, no obvious rhythmic pattern is played. All you do is strum an occasional chord. Due to the fact that it is "free" in style, there are many possible ways to accompany in this manner, depending on the song, and the effect that one wants to produce. Let us look at just one way in one song.

The Blue-tail Fly (Key of D)

```
    G                              G
    /                              /
WHEN I WAS YOUNG I USED TO WAIT

    /                              /
    D                              A7
UPON OLD MASTER AND PASS HIS PLATE

        G                              G
        /                              /
AND FETCH THE BOTTLE WHEN HE GOT DRY

    A7                  D
    /                   /
AND BRUSH AWAY THE BLUE-TAIL FLY
```

This is the verse of the song only; the chorus is in two-beat rhythm. Note that only thumb-strokes are indicated. These are not bass strings only; you simply strum the proper chord with your thumb, from low string to high across the guitar, across *all* the strings, that is, with the exception of the low E string in the chord, D, marked with an "x" in the chord diagram.

Again, be sure of your first note, and know the tune.

Also again, strike a D chord before you start, to orient yourself to the proper key and first note.

SIMPLE CHORD PROGRESSIONS

A chord *progression* is a series of chords which is used in a regular sequence so often that it is advisable to learn chords in such sequence.

In simple songs, it is found that the following sequence of chords occurs thousands of times: I, IV, V, I. I, means the chord based on the *first* note of any scale; IV means the chord based on the fourth note of any scale; V, means the chord based on the *fifth* note of any scale, then back to the I chord. (This is greatly oversimplified; for more detailed definitions, consult someone or a book on musical theory.)

To illustrate: In the key of C, a I chord is C, naturally; in the key of C, a IV chord would be F (C, D, E, F; I, II, III, IV); a V chord in C would then be G or G7.

These relationships hold true for any key; you simply count up four letters from any key, or five letters, to find the IV and V chords.

These progressions are all called *major* chord progressions. Since we are only to be concerned with a few major keys, let us note all the I, IV, V, I progressions in these keys.

	I	IV	V	I
Key of A:	A,	D,	E7,	A.
Key of C:	C,	F,	G7,	C.
Key of D:	D,	G,	A7,	D.
Key of E:	E,	A,	B7,	E.
Key of G:	G,	C,	D7,	G.

Why learn these in such a sequence? Because, once mastered, you will be able to accompany hundreds of simple songs, instead of just one or two.

Why not minor chord progressions? These also exist, but do not occur often enough in simple song accompaniments to bother with.

Note that the chords above repeat in different keys, at different localities. E.g., the C chord is I in the key of C, but is IV in the key of G.

Why different keys? To enable songs to be done lower or higher in pitch, that is all.

Many times, these progressions occur exactly in the above order in a song, but not always.

And now, try playing the three songs suggested thus far, in other keys above, replacing the chords within the song by the proper chords in the new key. In music, to play the same song in a new key is called *transposing*. Can you figure out the right chords in other keys for these songs?

The Capo. This is a gadget which permits easier transposition, or, key-changing. By clamping around a *fret* it raises the pitch of the guitar strings *one half-tone per fret*, e.g., if the Capo is around the *first fret* at the top, then the guitar strings are raised one half-tone in pitch; therefore, if you played the C chord you would really be playing C-sharp or D-flat. And so on for other chords and the Capo on other frets. In short, the Capo lets you play the easier chords in the more obscure keys.

CONCLUSION

Having shown one example of the three main types of folk song accompaniment, three-beat, two-beat, and free-style, there remains, in the limited space here, nothing but some concluding remarks.

Most songs in this book can be played according to the method outlined thus far, either by yourself, or with a little help from someone else. *Incidentally, any song in this book can be tried in free-style first, before rhythmically.* Then try the songs here in the two-beat or three-beat rhythms, except those marked "Freely," which are best played in free-style.

Listen to records of these songs; it is a fine way to pick up accompaniment hints and different styles of playing.

Do try to pick up the rudiments of music theory, plus the elements, at least, of reading a melody line. It is very easy, and will help you learn new songs.

I have said before, and I say again: be patient, and don't get discouraged. Keep at it, and soon your fingers will suddenly do as you wish.

You do not have to practice like a virtuoso violinist; but try to do a little *every day*; even fifteen minutes every day *without exception* will produce results surprisingly fast.

Try to get together with other beginners to exchange ideas and techniques, and to obtain answers for puzzling questions.

I have stated above somewhere that ten is the usual minimum age to begin; yet, I have seen a six-year-old boy playing chords surprisingly well. The only generality that holds in music is to enjoy it.

INDEX OF FIRST LINES

A farmer was ploughing his field one day 41
Alas, my love, you do me wrong 64
As I walked out in the streets of Laredo 134
As I walked out one evening 43
As I was out walking one morning for pleasure 53
As I went out walking down Paradise Street 11
Black, black, black is the color of my true love's hair 8
Chickens a-crowin' on Sourwood Mountain 126
Children, go, I will send thee 100
Down in the valley, the valley so low 28
Every morning at seven o'clock 30
Every night when the sun goes down 36
Eyes like a morning star, cheeks like a rose 21
Father and I went down to camp 153
Frankie and Johnnie were lovers 48
Go tell Aunt Rhody 57
Have you seen my Cindy? 19
Here I sit on Buttermilk Hill 92
He's got the whole world in His hand 74
"Hi," said the little leather-winged bat 98
How do you think I started in life? 128
I am a roving gambler 120
I gave my love a cherry, that has no stone 118
I got an old mule and her name is Sal 60
I know my love by her way of walking 78
I know where I'm goin' 80
I made up my mind in the early morn 140
I met her in Venezuela 147
I ride an old paint 82
If I had wings like Noah's dove 38
I'll give to you a paper of pins 112
I'm goin' down the road feelin' bad 58
I'm gone away, for to stay a little while 84
I'm just a poor, wayfaring stranger 149
In eighteen hundred and forty-one 114
In Scarlet town, where I was born 4
It takes a worried man to sing a worried song 151

I've wandered all over this country 2
Jesse James was a boy who killed many a man 88
Joshua fought the battle of Jericho 93
Lou, Lou, skip to my Lou 124
Love, oh love, oh careless love 18
Oh, don't you remember, sweet Betsy from Pike 136
Oh, freedom, freedom 108
Oh, give me a home, where the buffalo roam 76
Oh Shenando', I love your daughter 122
Oh, the candidate's a dodger, a well-known dodger 25
Oh, why don't I work like the other men do? 66
On Springfield Mountain there did dwell 132
On the first day of Christmas 142
On top of Old Smoky 110
Once I was a bachelor, I lived all alone 46
Once on a time there lived a man, his name was Peter Grey 116
Sittin' on the ice till my feet get cold, honey 23
So we'll go no more a-roving so late into the night 156
Sometimes I feel like a motherless child 106
Spanish is the loving tongue 130
Take this hammer (huh!) carry it to the captain 68
The frog went a-courtin' 51
The keeper would a-hunting go 95
There were three brothers in merry Scotland 72
'Tis advertised in Boston, New York, and Buffalo 13
Tam Pierce, Tam Pierce, lend me your gray mare 138
Uncle Reuben caught a coon, done gone 145
We were forty miles from Albany 34
Well, last Monday morning, Lawd 62
Well, you wake up in the morning 104
What shall we do with a drunken sailor? 32
When I was a little boy, my mother always told me 70
When I was apprenticed in London 9
When I was young, I used to wait upon old Master 15
When Israel was in Egypt land 55
When John Henry was a little baby 90
When the farmer comes to town 39
Where did you come from? 22
Where have you been all the day, Randal, my son? 102
Why come ye hither, invaders, your mind what madness fills? 6
Will you wear white, oh, my dear 86
Wilt thou come with me, sweet Tibbie Dunbar? 158
With rue my heart is laden 160